Twayne's United States Authors Series

Sylvia E. Bowman, *Editor*

INDIANA UNIVERSITY

Clifford Odets

CLIFFORD ODETS

by R. BAIRD SHUMAN

Duke University

 30

Twayne Publishers, Inc. :: New York

This book is dedicated to

MARTHA HEASLEY COX
and to
H. CHARLES HUTCHINGS, II
and to
the memory of
EDWIN COURTLANDT BOLLES

Preface

IN HIS RECENT BOOK, *Writers on the Left,* Daniel Aaron calls Clifford Odets "the 'Golden Boy' of the Left theater." While Aaron makes this designation in a context dealing with the 1930's, it is apparent that most people who remember Odets in the 1960's think of him in just such terms. As a result, much has been written which would suggest that Odets has been in a state of continuous decline from the time of such significant and successful social plays as *Waiting for Lefty* and *Awake and Sing!* down to the present day. All too little that has been written gives fair consideration to the fact that Odets has very much broadened his scope in the years following his initial successes—or to the fact that he has become more artistically conscious during these years.

A full understanding of Odets' plays is dependent upon the willingness of the audience to realize that the author is very often writing allegorically. In *The Flowering Peach* the allegory is more obvious than in such plays as *Golden Boy, Night Music,* or *Waiting for Lefty;* however, there is allegorical significance in most of Odets' work. To ignore this is to shut out much of the essence of what the author is saying. If one understands Odets' allegory, he will become aware that the author is as socially conscious in his later plays as he was in the early ones. In the later plays he chooses to write of problems with which the average playgoer is less concerned than was the average play- goer of the 1930's when the horrors of the Depression were evident to anyone who walked down the main street of an American city or town. However, on the allegorical level, the later plays are perhaps more universally relevant than the early ones. The Noah story, beautifully redacted in *The Flowering Peach,* deals with the question of the survival of mankind. In 1962, this question is in the forefront of many minds, for the onset of the atomic era has brought with it much speculation upon man's ability to survive. While *Golden Boy* and *Waiting for*

Lefty were concerned with the general questions of lost integrity on a somewhat personal level and of man's ability to survive economically, *The Flowering Peach* is concerned with man's ability to survive biologically.

Odets has never lost his talent for writing a good play. His ability to capture the cadences of contemporary speech and to reproduce them with poetic as well as social impact has made him worthy of a position of honor in American drama. But beyond this, Odets has consistently shown a profound respect for and understanding of human dignity. He may write of social forces from a somewhat negative point of view, but even his unsympathetic characters are written of from a more or less positive point of view. For example, in *Golden Boy*, Moody, eager to exploit Joe Bonaparte, is doing so only as a reaction to the desperate social situation in which he finds himself.

In recent years there has been a notable waning in Odets' productivity. This is due in part, perhaps, to the unsympathetic critical response to some of his later plays. In this study I have been concerned to a degree with presenting the critical reception of the plays. I have felt justified in doing this in order to point out the amount of disagreement which has existed among competent critics in regard to the quality of what Odets has written, as well as to indicate the general level at which most of the critics have viewed his work. It is obvious that only a handful of critics—Harold Clurman, John Gassner, John Mason Brown—have probed very far beyond the literal level in their estimates of the plays. As a result, the critics of the later plays have often expressed their concern with Odets' loss of social vitality in his later writing.

This book has done little to trace the literary and philosophical influences which motivated Odets in his writing, because specula-tion on such points would necessarily be based upon spurious assumptions. It is evident that the social and economic forces of the 1930's were basic to his outlook. His temperament and social conscience were alien to the prosperity and easy living of the 1920's; it was only with the onset of the Depression that he found the material for writing. He could understand the fear and suffering and insecurity of those whose very lives were suddenly imperiled by economic disaster in a land of plenty. He could feel one with the masses; he could capture their most intimate thoughts and apprehensions and could put them into words with strength and vitality.

Odets learned the theatre from the inside. In *The Fervent Years*, Harold Clurman tells in detail of Odets' long and devoted apprenticeship in the Group Theatre. With every role that the young actor learned, with every line that he spoke, he was learning the craft of playwrighting, for Odets was instinctively the playwright first and the actor second. To trace the literary influences on Odets' writing, it is necessary only to refer to the roster of plays which the Group Theatre produced from its inception to 1935; these were Odets' developmental years, his years of searching. From the Group presentations he learned much.

Fundamental to his development, too, was his association with the young liberals who were a part of the Group Theatre. Odets grappled with political philosophies at a time when the economic plight of the masses was daily flooding in upon his experience. He espoused communism as a panacea, only to reject it within less than a year in favor of a modified form of socialism.

This book represents the first full-length study of Odets and of his plays. Ideally, it will be superseded in time by a book which deals with more than the eleven plays treated here; for Odets' work is by no means done. He still has much to say which will be relevant to men who, having found a solution to many of the basic questions which perplexed them in the 1930's, now stand on the tenuous ground between war and peace, between survival and mass annihilation.

R. BAIRD SHUMAN

Los Gatos, California
February 14, 1962

Acknowledgments

Grateful acknowledgment is made to Clifford Odets for his many courtesies to me during the course of this study. Miss Sylvia Bowman, editor of *Twayne's United States Authors Series* must also be warmly and gratefully commended for her prompt, conscientious, and careful editing of this volume.

Anita Block has graciously granted me permission to use excerpts from her study, *The Changing World in Plays and Theatre* (Little, Brown and Company, 1939); and Simon and Schuster, Inc., has granted me permission to use excerpts from Eleanor Flexner's *American Playwrights: 1918-1938*. Harold Clurman has granted permission to quote from his introductions which appear in *Six Plays of Clifford Odets* and from *The Fervent Years*, as well as from a number of his articles. I am grateful to Joseph Wood Krutch, who permitted me to quote from numerous reviews of his which appeared in *Nation*. The *New Yorker* has generously permitted me to quote from its reviews of a number of Odets' plays.

A deep debt of gratitude is due the following University of Pennsylvania professors who aided and encouraged the writer, while giving him valuable criticism and assistance: Edgar L. Potts, Matthew Black, and Gerald Weales. For their encouragement and assistance the writer is also deeply grateful to Professors Edwin C. Bolles, Allan Chester, James J. Clark, Earle T. Crooker, Charles D. Ludlum, Jr., Ralph C. Most, and the late E. Lee Goldsborough.

For calling the writer's attention to various obscure sources relating to Odets, Mrs. C. L. Davis, Mr. H. Charles Hutchings II, and Mr. Kirk G. Rummel must be commended.

Contents

Chronology

1906 Clifford Odets born in Philadelphia, Pennsylvania, July 18.

1912 Family moves to New York City.

1921- Student in Morris High School, New York City.
1923

1923- Various small acting positions, often in juvenile roles for
1930 the Theatre Guild.

1929 Understudy to Spencer Tracy in Broadway production of
Conflict.

1930 Joins the Group Theatre.

1935 Wrote and appeared in *Waiting for Lefty;* it wins George
Pierce Baker Drama Cup, Yale University, and New
Theatre–New Masses Theatre Contest. Completed *Awake
and Sing!* and *Paradise Lost;* wrote *Till the Day I Die.*
Made protest trip to Cuba.

1936 Wrote *I Can't Sleep.*

1937 Married Luise Rainer, January 8. Wrote film scenario of
The General Died at Dawn. Wrote *Golden Boy* and
Silent Partner.

1938 Wrote *Rocket to the Moon.*

1939 Publication of *Six Plays of Clifford Odets.*

1940 Wrote *Night Music.*

1941 Wrote *Clash by Night.* Divorced from Luise Rainer.

1942 Wrote film scenario for *Humoresque.*

1943 Wrote film scenario for *None But the Lonely Heart,* also
directed this film. Married Bette Grayson, May 14.

1944 Wrote scenario for *Deadline at Dawn.*

1948 Wrote *The Big Knife.*

1950 Wrote *The Country Girl.*

1954 Wrote *The Flowering Peach.* Bette Grayson Odets dies.

1959 Directed *The Story on Page One.*

1961 Received Drama Award from the American Academy of Arts and Letters.

Clifford Odets

CHAPTER *1*

Odets the Man

I. *The Beginnings*

THE ONE HERO in the early plays of Clifford Odets is, in
the author's words, ". . . the entire American middle-class of
liberal tendency." Clifford, the eldest of three children of the
Jewish-American, middle-class family of Louis and Pearl
Geisinger Odets, was born in Philadelphia on July 18, 1906. He
had two sisters, Genevieve (born in 1910), later Mrs. Howard
Levy, and Florence (born in 1917).

Odets has been quoted as saying, "I was a worker's son until
the age of 12." His father had sold newspapers and peddled salt.
His mother worked for some time in a factory. During these
early years of the author's life, the family shuttled back and forth
between Philadelphia and the Bronx, where it finally settled
during Clifford's sixth year. It was in this year that Clifford
played his first dramatic role in a first grade production of
Cinderella at Public School Number 52. His part was that of
the charming prince. From this time forth the boy was determined
to be an actor and he spoke of little else.

In New York City the Odets family began to enjoy moderate
success. Mr. Odets rose from the position of feeder in a printery
to become the owner of the plant. The family lived in one of the
first apartment buildings in the Bronx that had an elevator. Early
in the second decade of the century, Mr. Odets bought a Maxwell
automobile, a sure sign of distinction and financial attainment
at this time. Mrs. Odets, who was unwell, vacationed in California
with her two daughters. The family was no longer of the working
class which Clifford was later to portray with such force and
vitality in his plays.

Speaking of his own childhood, Odets recalls, "I was a melancholy kid." At the age of fourteen, having completed his second year at Morris High School in New York City, he terminated his formal education because ". . . it was a waste of time." He tried to learn the printing business under his father's tutelage, but his interest in the theatre and in writing was so great that his father soon realized the futility of trying to push his son into the printing business and gave his reluctant consent to Clifford's going into acting. Clifford began his career in acting with the Drawing-Room Players, a neighborhood company which specialized in presenting one-act plays in the Heckscher Theatre in New York City. From this group he moved on to Harry Kemp's Poets' Theatre, a cooperative theatrical group whose plays were presented in a church basement at Fourth Street and Avenue A. Odets' net proceeds from one year of acting with this group amounted to slightly under twenty dollars; however, the experience gained during this year was inestimable. Frequently during this period Odets gave performances as a roving reciter, specializing in the poems of Rudyard Kipling and Robert Service. He also played in vaudeville for a dollar a night, wrote radio plays and gags, did some radio announcing, and worked with sound effects for a radio station.

In 1925, Odets formed his own company of actors composed chiefly of former members of the Drawing-Room Theatre, and with this group he presented sustaining programs on the radio for some time. Feeling within the Odets family often ran high during this period; Odets' work on his typewriter, which often continued far into the night, was a constant source of concern to his mother, and his father, in an outburst of temper, smashed his son's typewriter but later replaced it. At about this time the elder Odets sold his business for over two hundred thousand dollars and the family moved back to Philadelphia where it settled in the fashionable Oak Lane section of the city. Clifford, now doing stock company work, was on the road at this time playing the role of Abie in *Abie's Irish Rose.*

When the stock company with which he was playing found itself stranded and virtually penniless in Hawley, Pennsylvania, Odets was forced to return to the family home in Oak Lane; and for the next two years, he remained in the Philadelphia area, where he became a member of the Mae Desmond Stock Company. During this time he also wrote two brief radio plays, *Dawn,* which was not performed, and *At the Waterline,* which was presented by two New York radio stations as well as by Philadelphia's radio station WIP.

In 1929, when the opportunity came for Odets to understudy Spencer Tracy in the Broadway production of *Conflict,* he went to New York and in a short time became associated with the Theatre Guild with which he had previously had a brief association in 1923. In 1930 he played the juvenile lead in the road company of *Midnight* and later the same year he established what proved to be one of the most fruitful and compelling associations of his life: he joined the Group Theatre as a charter member.

II *Odets and the Group Theatre*

Odets was to be enormously affected by the philosophy of the Group Theatre, a fundamental part of which was that "there were to be no stars . . . not for the negative purpose of avoiding distinction, but because all distinction . . . was to be embodied in the production as a whole. The writer himself was to be no star either, for his play, the focus of our attention, was simply the instrument for capturing an idea that was always greater than that instrument itself."[1] The emphasis of the Group Theatre on the philosophy of each play it considered for presentation was so pronounced that Odets was, in the early years of his career as playwright, to be primarily concerned with the social content of his plays and secondarily with their dramatic structure. This is not to imply that the early Odets plays are structurally weak, but merely to point out that they are more consciously directed to social than to artistic ends.

In the winter of 1930, Odets was living in a room on West Eighty-second Street in New York City. Solitary and depressed, the young actor spent most of his time searching his own soul and thinking of the plight of the unfortunates about him, people beset by the problems which had grown out of the most serious economic depression ever to befall the United States. When the winter was over, he was gloomy and confused; in June, 1931, he left for Brookfield Center, Connecticut, where the Group Theatre was to begin rehearsals of its first production, Paul Green's *The House of Connelly*, scheduled to open in New York the following fall. During this time, Odets thought of writing a play to be titled *9-10 Eden Street*, which would be concerned with the intelligentsia of Philadelphia; but he abandoned this plan as his attention and energies were channeled more directly into the training program of the Group Theatre, whose actors had intensive classes in the fundamentals of acting, in special problems of acting, in speech and drama, in dramatic singing, and in dancing. The actors in the Group were almost totally absorbed in striving to strengthen their craft, hence this was a summer of very hard and continuous work as well as one of adjustment to a new and unique philosophy of the theatre.[2] The Group impinged upon every phase of a member's life. A writer for *Time Magazine* pointed out that "the Group . . . played father to its children, studied their habits."[3]

After *The House of Connelly* had opened at the Martin Beck Theatre in New York, Odets completed *9-10 Eden Street* and submitted it to the directors of the Group Theatre for critical reading. Harold Clurman, speaking for the Group, ". . . hardly thought of it as a play, or of its author as a potential playwright. It was a personal document." Clurman felt that the play ". . . gave evidence of internal injury in the writer. . . . Something in his past life had hurt him. He was doubled up in pain now, and in his pain he appeared to be shutting out the world." Clurman continued, "His perception was disturbed because everything was seen in relation to his hurt."[4] This criticism, while not unique in regard to early works of young authors, was very telling in regard to Odets as well as to his future production. *9-10 Eden Street* was never produced.

During the season of 1931-32, Odets played minor roles in Group productions of *The House of Connelly*, in Claire and Paul Sifton's *1931—*, and in Maxwell Anderson's *Night over Taos*. He was not generally considered a gifted actor then any more than he had been some five or six years before, when his father had remarked to him, "You're not very good, you talk too fast," or when Rouben Mamoulian, after seeing him in a presentation of Čapek's *R. U R.*, had said very loudly, "He is no good!"

It had been a constant source of regret to Odets that he had not been trained from early childhood as a musician. His interest in music had always been intense. During the winter of 1931-32, he began to write a novel about a pianist who had lost his left hand in an accident. Although this novel was only fragmentary and was eventually destroyed by the author, it is significant to note that it provided a basis for his later play, *Golden Boy*.

The following year, while the Group summered at Dover Furnace, New York, Odets, virtually crippled from the "body classes" which were given to the members of the company by the choreographer Helen Tamiris, began to write a play about Beethoven. He wrote in his diary: "Here I am writing the Beethoven play, which when it is finished may not even be about Beethoven. Why not write something about the Greenberg family, something I know better, something that is closer to me?" This statement apparently germinated in the author's mind, and a few days later he entered in his diary the words, "I look at the baby that was me and rejoice." This series of events is a direct prelude to the writing of *Awake and Sing!*, which he was soon to begin.

As the Depression continued, Odets grew more and more concerned with the plight of the working and middle classes. He looked about him for ways of ameliorating the widespread suffering and privation of the masses during this period and suggested, in his writing, the outcomes of this quest. During this period J. Edward Bromberg of the Group Theatre, whom Odets called ". . . a man of the left who practiced what he preached," convinced the author to become a member of the Communist Party. This was in 1934, in the depths of the Depression when Odets was having a great struggle to exist. Odets' association with the Party continued for eight months; after that he discovered that the pressures which the Party tried to bring to bear upon his writing were stifling to him as an artist. He thereupon discontinued his membership in and his association with the Communist Party.

Joseph Wood Krutch has pointed out that ". . . [Odets] seems to have identified himself with the Communist Party only after he had begun to write. Unlike Mr. Lawson . . . his conversion did not deprive him of a subject and one of the most interesting things about his plays is the fact that he has managed to avoid rather more successfully than any of his fellows the tendency to assume almost automatically that a Communist play must treat directly one or another of the two or three situations which have come to be taken for granted as inevitable."⁵ Odets has claimed that his concern for the middle class largely represents his position as "a man of the opposition." His interests in and sympathy for the masses he attributes largely to his first reading in 1918 of Victor Hugo's *Les Miserables*.

After he had bolted from the Communist Party, Odets still admitted that he sympathized with it ideologically; he maintained a belief in the need for "some kind of socialism," but declared, "I am a Liberal, not a Communist." Odets' major social concern as an artist became that of expressing and exposing ". . . the frauds of middle-class civilization, deprived by its economic insecurity of its former status and becoming aware that most of its cherished ideals no longer correspond to realities."⁶ He succeeded in using the stage as a platform from which he could express with vehemence and effectivenesss his concepts of contemporary society. In an interview he conceded that ". . . all plays, just like all literature and drama, are essentially propaganda of one sort or another. All creative endeavor, from the Homeric sagas down to the films of Maurice Chevalier, exists to recommend some specialized type or conduct of life. My problem and business in the world is to present truth dramatically, appealingly, and entertainingly . . . The presentation of truth without any editorialization is the most revolutionary thing in the world."⁷ Odets wanted to write about what was around him. He thought that ". . . this is a wonderful time to write. Hart Crane jumped off a boat crying—This is no time for poets—He was wrong. This is no time for weakness, but it is certainly a time for poets."

In the fall of 1932, when the Group returned from Dover Furnace, Odets and several others from the company moved into a large, poorly heated apartment on New York's West Side. The summer had proved to be a personal revelation to Odets, who finally began to realize what sort of plays he had to write and what sort of people he had to write about. He crouched over his typewriter in the Group apartment, dressed in his warmest woolens, blew on his hands to warm them, and wrote about the sort of people he had known from childhood and about the pressures which were now forced upon them by an all-pervasive economic depression. Whenever he had completed four or five pages of typescript, he would summon the other occupants of the apartment into the kitchen, the only warm room in the flat, and there they would stage impromptu performances of portions of the script. It was during one such performance that the Group Theatre director Harold Clurman came by and was so favorably impressed by what he heard that he invited Odets to move into his apartment in Greenwich Village to complete the writing of his play there.

During this winter, Clurman and Odets spent much time walking the streets at night, sitting in Stewart's Cafeteria on Sheridan Square, talking with people, studying them. The two sometimes went to burlesque houses which ". . . had no sex lure for us; they had the appeal of lurid dejection. Somehow we felt close to the down-in-the-mouth comedians and oddly tender about the bruised beauties of the chorus." Odets, according to Clurman, ". . . reacted to everything, not with words or articulate knowledge, but with his body. His senses were extraordinarily alive, although he was not professionally 'sensitive.' To be near him was like being near a stove on which a whole range of savory foods was standing ready to be served."

When this winter had ended, Odets had completed his first significant full-length play, *Awake and Sing!*, but it was then entitled *I've Got the Blues*. And, as R. S. Warshow later noted in *Commentary*, "What he knows about Jews is in *Awake and Sing!*" Writing this play very much helped Odets to crystallize in his own mind his ultimate purpose in writing. In a *New York Times* interview in 1935 he is quoted as saying that through *Awake and Sing!* ". . . I understood clearly that my interest was not in the presentation of an individual's problems, but in those of a whole class . . . the task was to find a theatrical form with which to express the mass as hero." The problem of finding the form was solved, partially at least, in *Awake and Sing!* and later, more fully perhaps, in *Paradise Lost*.

The most exciting and dynamic year in Clifford Odets' life was 1935. Before the year was half out, Odets had gained a national reputation as a dramatist through his play *Waiting for Lefty*, and he had seen successful presentations in New York of

Awake and Sing! and of *Till the Day I Die.* Critical recognition of the young playwright's significance and potential was almost immediate. John Mason Brown called *Awake and Sing!* ". . . well-balanced, meticulously observed, always interesting and ultimately quite moving drama." Of Odets' method he said that Odets ". . . seems to have employed a machine gun rather than a pen," and he predicted that "Unless all signs fail in fair weather, Clifford Odets has the stuff." The *Literary Digest* ran a bold type headline which declared, "Two Short Social Plays—and a Long One—Transform a Young Actor into a Vigorous, Articulate Playwright, Boiling with Protest against the Structure of His Times." Stark Young called him ". . . the only new [dramatist] discovered in a good many seasons. . . . Mr. Odets is one of the few American playwrights who is worth thinking about at all."

In the midst of such heartening acclaim, Odets suffered the loss of his mother who died in May, 1935, at the age of forty-seven. Shortly after her death the young playwright headed an investigatory commission which was ". . . irreconcilably opposed to the domination of Cuba by American financial and industrial interests." Almost in corroboration of Krutch's statement early in the year that ". . . he has the full courage of his convictions," Odets led the commission to Cuba aboard the *S.S. Oriente* to verify newspaper reports that under the Mendieta regime civil liberties had been virtually suspended in the country. The members of the commission, including Odets, were met at the pier in Havana, placed under arrest, and forced to return to the United States as soon as possible. They were termed undesirable aliens and were confined in the Tiscornia Immigration Station. When they arrived back in New York on July 6, 1935, they were met at the dock by some three hundred sympathizers and a brass band. The group left the ship and went immediately to consult the Cuban Consul General in order to lodge a formal protest. They also publicly criticized the United States Embassy in Havana for not having intervened to have them released. Odets, inflamed over the incident, hoped to bring it to the attention of the public in a play which, although it was finally written, never progressed beyond the first rough draft and was, of course, never produced.[8]

Shortly before Odets embarked on his protest pilgrimage to

Cuba, he was awarded the George Pierce Baker Cup by the Yale University Drama School in recognition of *Waiting for Lefty*, which had already won the New Theatre–New Masses Drama Contest. By the middle of June, 1935, thirty-two Theatre League groups had produced *Waiting for Lefty* throughout the United States. But by now the play had become a target for suppression such as had not been witnessed since the Red scare of the 1920's. Seven cities—among them Boston, New Haven, and Newark, New Jersey—banned *Waiting for Lefty*. In Hollywood the director of the play was kidnapped and badly beaten. As a result, the air was filled with protests from many quarters, including the reputedly conservative Authors' League of America. The play weathered this storm of reactionary suppression and, to a degree, even prospered because of it. Audiences throughout the nation were at this time singularly receptive to social drama in general and to Odets' plays in particular.

Odets was dedicated to literature containing social impact. He recognized Albert Bein as a crusader of his own ilk and wrote after the opening of *Let Freedom Ring*, "I don't know what makes a great American play. But I damn well know a good American play when I see it; and I saw it when I went to see Albert Bein's *Let Freedom Ring*. . . . It is highly literate, deeply entertaining, hot with life, juicy with American characters. Its meaning is the meaning of American life today." This last sentence indicates to a large extent what Odets was trying to achieve in his own writing during this period. It is essential to an understanding of Odets that one realize that his concern is chiefly with "American life today." Even in his adaptation of the Noah story, *The Flowering Peach*, his concerns are current; the ancient setting is an allegorical one.

After the success which was registered by *Waiting for Lefty, Till the Day I Die*, and *Awake and Sing!*, Odets returned to a play on which he had worked and completed two acts in 1934, *Paradise Lost*. When Harold Clurman first saw, in December, 1934, the two acts of the play which had then been completed, he had expressed his faith in the work, but Lee Strasberg was dubious about it. Odets, who proclaimed this to be his favorite play, offered to set about raising money for its

CLIFFORD ODETS

production, but Strasberg said, "You don't seem to understand, Cliff. We don't like your play. We don't like it." Because Strasberg was one of the three directors of the Group Theatre, his decision, for the time, stood. Nevertheless, after Odets' three major triumphs in 1935, the Group decided that it owed to him the production of *Paradise Lost.* As it turned out, the presentation of this play represented a turning point in the life and career of Clifford Odets; for, as will be seen, it provided him with reason to leave New York and go to Hollywood.

Odets and Mr. Clurman had, with the success of the three plays produced in the spring of 1935, moved from their small Village apartment into a penthouse on University Place where Odets was surrounded by the music and books which he so deeply loved. One day Odets returned to his penthouse from uptown and told Clurman that he had been offered five hundred dollars a week by a Hollywood scout. At this time, despite the widespread recognition of his ability, Odets' earnings were still relatively modest. He was now strongly tempted to leave New York and asked Clurman whether it was not unrealistic to turn down what seemed to him a princely offer. Clurman replied that he didn't think it was unrealistic to reject the offer because he was sure that Odets could command much more if he waited. By April, 1935, Metro-Goldwyn-Mayer had made Odets a firm offer of three thousand dollars a week and had indicated that it might be willing to go even beyond this offer. Odets resisted the lure of Hollywood as the offers mounted. By summer he had been offered four thousand dollars a week, but he was unwilling to forsake the Group and remained firm in his refusals.

Paradise Lost opened in the fall and, as will be seen in the chapter dealing with the play, was a distinct commercial failure. Now Odets was able to rationalize his going to Hollywood on the ground that he was doing so in order to save this, his favorite play. He negotiated for some time through his agent, but now that he had produced a failure, the most that he could command was twenty-five hundred dollars a week. Odets was unhappy and, to a degree, ashamed at leaving the Group, even though he was clear in his assertion that his trip to Hollywood was to be short and exploratory in nature. However, Hollywood represented "sin" to Odets, as is pointed out by Clurman's record, in *The Fervent Years,* of a conversation with him shortly before he left for the West Coast. Stella Adler had said, "I feel that I need to sin, and you [Clurman] make me feel I have no right to sin." Odets, pacing about the room, stopped suddenly and shouted, "She's right! She's right!" and thereupon announced his decision to leave the Group temporarily. The members were unhappy and resentful that Odets should leave, even though they realized that by doing so he could lighten the financial burden which the Group had incurred in producing *Paradise Lost.*

Once in Hollywood, Odets sent four thousand dollars back to the Group to buttress his commercially weak play. He remained in Hollywood for the better part of a year and did an adaptation of *The General Died at Dawn* for the films. It was this film that occasioned the now famous remark of Frank S. Nugent who, writing in the *New York Times,* asked, "Odets, where is thy sting?"

With the appearance of this film, New York critics generally agreed that the predictions which some of them had made earlier had come true: Odets had come full circle and was finished as a playwright. Few considered that he might have had a deeper underlying motive for going to Hollywood than that of gaining wealth, for to most of them Hollywood also represented "sin." However, Eric Bentley, writing much later in *The Playwright as Thinker,* noted that ". . . before the talkies were a decade old, even the kind of people who had earlier despised the screen began to see in it the successor to the living actor. In this belief, it is said, Clifford Odets left Broadway for Hollywood: the drama was a thing of the past; the future belonged to the motion picture." Perhaps Mr. Bentley imputes too much to Odets in this statement, but it certainly is not fair to assume, as so many critics have, that the author had simply sold out as an artist in order to achieve financial success. To make such an assumption is to oversimplify Odets' motives.

Although Odets' life in Hollywood was comfortable, it was somewhat unrewarding to him personally and artistically. He complained to an interviewer for *Time Magazine* at that time, when asked about the motion picture industry and its relation to him as a writer, "They want to emasculate me." As late as 1959 he commented that ". . . unless you are a Mozart or a Bach,

CLIFFORD ODETS

pieces to order (movies out here) have only a slight value. There are rare exceptions to this rule, but I don't know one in my own writing, not being Mozart or Bach." However, it is obvious that Odets had mixed feelings regarding the effect of Hollywood upon the artist, for in 1959 he also told Joe Hyams, who was interviewing him for the *New York Herald Tribune*, "What the critics don't realize is I picked up half my technique here. . . . The movies are a brilliant training school for a dramatic writer."

During his early days in Hollywood, Odets met Luise Rainer, the rising Austrian film star, and on January 8, 1937, the two were married. Their marriage was terminated by divorce in 1941. In July, 1937, the couple returned to New York, where Odets hoped to see his wife star in one of his plays.

The interlude in Hollywood had broadened Odets' outlook, even though it had not at this time contributed significantly to his stature as an artist. He was sought now not only as a playwright but also as a teacher. He participated in a course on screen treatment which was offered by the Division of General Education of New York University. Among the other participants in this course were such rising dramatists as Sidney Kingsley and Sidney Howard.

From the time that *Awake and Sing!* was presented until 1941, Odets carried on his shoulders much of the responsibility of the Group Theatre. In its later years, his were the only really successful plays which the Group produced. In the summer of 1937, when the Group was in especially grave financial straits, Odets wrote *Golden Boy* for it, and the play was produced during the following season. Not only did the author permit the Group to produce the play, which had a successful seven-month run on Broadway, but he and his wife subsidized the cost of the production in the amount of five thousand dollars and took a twenty-five per cent financial interest in the play. This interest, as it turned out, gave them a handsome return of some two thousand dollars a week during the play's New York run. Hollywood later paid Odets seventy-five thousand dollars for the movie rights to the play. During this same time Odets was working on what he had said would ". . . be the best labor play ever produced in the country or any other country"; but this play, *The Silent Partner*, still remains unproduced.

By the beginning of the 1938-39 theatrical season, the Group Theatre was in a very favorable financial situation, largely because of the success of *Golden Boy,* which was now put on the road for what proved to be a highly successful tour. For the first time in its history, the Group Theatre was able to guarantee the salaries of sixteen of its players for the entire year. At this time, Odets ". . . again forsaking the easier money of Hollywood for the sake of his art, delivered a play of middle-aged romance called *Rocket to the Moon,* which his severest critics were ready to admit contained some of the most forceful writing in his career." The play, though not a huge success, did attract sizeable audiences, partly because of the new Group Theatre policy of selling large blocks of tickets through charitable and cultural organizations. When *Rocket to the Moon* seemed to have run its course, the Group revived *Awake and Sing!* which, having run for one hundred thirty-seven performances in 1935, now ran for forty-four additional performances, all very well attended.

If George Kaufman and Edna Ferber had had Odets in mind when they wrote into *Stage Door* a radical young playwright who had gone to Hollywood and grown rather vulgarly and disgustingly rich, they now had cause to reconsider, as did many of the gloomy prophets who thought Odets was through as a writer for the legitimate stage. Odets was now showing himself to be fundamentally an artist whose basic concern was his craft.

In the autumn of 1939, the Modern Library issued a volume entitled *Six Plays of Clifford Odets,* with an introduction by the author and with an appendix consisting of introductions by Harold Clurman to three of the plays contained in the volume. The collection contained *Waiting for Lefty, Awake and Sing!, Till the Day I Die, Paradise Lost, Golden Boy,* and *Rocket to the Moon.* On the appearance of this volume, a *New Republic* critic, O. Ferguson, commented that ". . . through the six plays one thing is clear; Clifford Odets can do just about what he wants to because he has the right eye—what he has seen makes a storehouse of vivid people and things and action from the immediate world—and because he has theatrical genius." In a mere four and a half years, Odets had captured the imagination of a receptive public and had skyrocketed to fame.

The production of *Paradise Lost* by the Group Theatre had

been a turning point of one kind in Odets' life. He had left New York and gone, almost shamefacedly, to Hollywood. But he did this in an attempt to save a play in which he had great faith and to aid the company producing it. As a prodigal son, Odets had returned to the Group at the earliest opportunity and had remained dedicated to it and to its unique theatrical ideals. However, another sort of turning point occurred during the season of 1939-40 when the Group produced the most recent Odets effort, *Night Music*. The play was tender, sometimes inchoate and slightly less than coherent, but it was a play well suited to that crucial period before America's entry into a second world conflict. As literature, the play, coming at the beginning of a new decade, was more suggestive of the 1920's than of the 1930's, for its basic theme was homelessness, its ultimate problem one of personal isolation.[9] Odets conceived of the play as a "song cycle on a given theme." The play is pervaded by a melodic quality and is highly suggestive of what Odets referred to as New York's rhythm which he called in an interview recorded in the *New York Times Magazine*, ". . . the most intense in the world. It picks you up very high and lets you down very gently. . . . the city always goes *allegro con brio*." Odets felt very strongly about the production of *Night Music* (the score of which was written by Hanns Eisler), and he took an active role in the rehearsals, giving extra attention to the direction which Harold Clurman had undertaken.

When Odets handed over the play to the director, he had said that it was to be presented exactly as he had written it. Nothing was to be cut or changed. However, by opening night the script had been pruned by half an hour with the author's full consent. The opening in Boston was hindered by extremely adverse weather conditions, and Odets began to be apprehensive about the play's future on Broadway. He suggested a wholesale cutting of entire scenes, but Clurman was firm in his opposition of this. The cast remained most enthusiastic and sanguine about the play which, during its entire run, was warmly received by the members of the Group.

Night Music opened at the Broadhurst, a large New York theatre. Opening night tickets were, at Odets' insistence, placed on sale at $4.40, quite in opposition to the Group principle of keeping the price of tickets within the reach of the average man. The opening was a thorough disappointment; and the press, while praising the excellence of the Group performance, had few kind words to say in regard to the play itself. Odets suffered a personal injury more deep than any which he had hitherto had to bear. He began to feel that the atmosphere of the Group was constricting, and Clurman himself felt very uneasy about the Group's relations with the playwright and the future of the Group Theatre as an institution. All of the members seemed to be going off in their own separate directions, and new actors were not appearing to replace them.

In August, 1940, Odets told Clurman very frankly that he was tired of the Group actors and did not intend to be impeded by a sense of loyalty to them. Clurman was in a state of mental turmoil and sought escape, first in Hollywood, then back in New York, then in Cape Cod; he was unable to settle down, unwilling to let the Group dissolve, yet not sure of his ability to hold it together.

As Irwin Shaw's *Retreat to Pleasure* was approaching dress rehearsal, Clurman was invited to dine with Odets at his Beekman Place apartment. During the course of the evening, Odets made known his desire to produce his new play, *Clash by Night*, with Lee Strasberg as director. The production was to be under the Group auspices, but Odets was to supply or arrange for most of the backing of the show and would, as a result, receive the bulk of any profits which might accrue from it. Clurman, who had just been offered a six-month Hollywood contract, was quite willing at this point to leave the Group in the hands of Odets and Strasberg.

As it turned out, Odets finally had to go far afield in order to find the financial backing which *Clash by Night* required. Billy Rose eventually put up the necessary capital, but he demanded such a favorable return on his investment that there would, under this arrangement, be no money left for the Group. Then Rose insisted that the name of the Group Theatre not be used in billing the play; as it turned out, *Clash by Night* had only a minor connection with the Group, from which only two of the cast members were drawn. This marked the final disintegration of the Group Theatre and the end of Odets' most fruitful and satisfying artistic period.

III *After the Group Theatre*

With the cessation of Group activities, Odets returned to Hollywood, where he did three scenarios in as many years. These films were *Humoresque* (1942); *None But the Lonely Heart* (1943), which he also directed; and *Deadline at Dawn* (1944). It was during this period that his interest in directing grew and that the next distinct phase of his life began. Also, during this period on May 14, 1943, he married Betty Grayson who was to bear him two children, Nora and Walt. Mrs. Odets died in 1954.

Odets did not bring a new play to Broadway until the appearance of *The Big Knife* late in the 1948-49 theatrical season. This play was largely a commentary on Hollywood. It was generally well received by the critics, although they always tended to make comparisons between the present and the past Odets whose dramatically successful beginning in the theatre was notable. John Mason Brown, writing in the *Saturday Review of Literature*, astutely observed of Odets: "Instead of being compared unfavorably with his betters, he has been compared unfavorably with himself."

The American National Theatre Association (ANTA) revived *Golden Boy* in 1952 with the author directing. The run was highly successful. The critic for *Saturday Review of Literature* felt that ". . . the revival of the Odets classic . . . should run about as long as those connected with it wish it to." While it was noted by W. H. Beyer in *School and Society* that "Odets, as the director, emphasizes the play's exaggerations," it was generally conceded that his directing was effective and at times brilliant.

Perhaps Odets' most successful effort in directing was displayed in the production of his play, *The Country Girl*. The play was originally written for Charles Coburn, but, as it turned out, the part written for him was not suitable. In directing the play, Odets was said by a writer for *Life Magazine* to have behaved ." . . . like a symphony conductor, urging and cajoling actors and exploding with approval when they do well." His direction was from the character's point of view and his chief concern was with character behavior. This is evident from his statement in regard to his approach to writing the play: "I don't lay out plays—I lay out characters."

In directing, Odets showed much of the influence of the Group Theatre and the Stanislavsky method; his approach was different with each actor. He took actors aside and talked with them quietly, ". . . gently, like a father teaching his children to walk," telling them about the character they were portraying, always describing, never demonstrating. His own philosophy of directing was succinctly stated in an interview recorded in *Theatre Arts Monthly:* "To my mind there are three ways to direct a play. First, *critically.* That is, to analyze each scene and moment for the actors. Secondly, to direct it *synthetically,* to take the material of the play and create something new out of it by enlarging it. Thirdly, and the best way, is a combination of both."

Odets' last stage play, *The Flowering Peach,* is a free adaptation of the biblical story of Noah. The critical reaction varied from one extreme to another. Eric Bentley called it ". . . the best American play I have ever reviewed in these [*New Republic*] columns." But Gerald Weales writing in *Commentary* began his review with the words, "It would not be unusual to report that Odets had written a very bad play . . . but it is sad that his version of the Noah legend should be so very dull."

Odets has yet to produce the three plays for which, in 1950, he had plans and titles, and it now seems doubtful that *By the Sea, The Seasons,* and *The Tides of Fundy* will be forthcoming. In 1959 Odets directed an original film, *The Story on Page One,* which received generally restrained reviews.

Now living in California, the author takes pleasure in painting water colors and has had an exhibition of his work. He also collects works of art and has well over two hundred canvases in his collection. He paints late at night in his basement, chiefly to overcome ". . . the pressure this evil, vicious society imposes [and to] cultivate my innocence and . . . ignorance." Much of his time is also spent listening to his records, among which works by Beethoven and Mozart predominate. Music is very much in the forefront of his mind and his conversations are interspersed with musical allusions.

Now in his mid-fifties, Clifford Odets can look back upon a record of accomplishment unique in the history of twentieth-century American drama.

CHAPTER 2

Odets and the Proletariat

I *Some Background to Proletarian Writing*

PROLETARIAN LITERATURE may be defined as that which is primarily concerned with presenting a sympathetic and understanding portrayal of the lives, problems, and sufferings of the working class while at the same time exposing the social injustices and inequalities of an age. Some proletarian writers suggest remedies for the conditions about which they write; some merely present the problems in their grossest aspects and suggest no realistic remedies.

Proletarian literature reached its height in the United States in the period between the great economic depression of 1929 and the beginning of World War II. It is during this period that such proletarian dramatists as Clifford Odets, Albert Bein, Albert Maltz, and Elmer Rice rose to prominence. But proletarian literature had been written before their day. Indeed, even before a proletariat existed as such, each age produced literature which was concerned with the oppression of the underling by the overlord, be he an industrial baron or the lord of a feudal stronghold. *Deor's Lament* in the Old English period presents the disheartening plight of the court poet who loses favor with his lord and is subsequently replaced. Dickens tells his readers of the wretched conditions of young David Copperfield and of the social inequalities which made the life of Oliver Twist an unhappy one, just as a century before Samuel Richardson had written in *Pamela* of the trials of a young girl trying to make her way in life without sacrificing her virtue. Frank Norris presents the case of the farmers who are battling the railroad in *The Octopus*, while Theodore Dreiser, like a Richardson of the twentieth century, concerns himself with the adaptation of a farm girl to an industrial society which would exploit her kind in both *Sister Carrie* and *Jennie Gerhardt;* social pressures forced the outcomes in both books.

Much proletarian literature presents very pat solutions to the social and economic problems with which it is concerned. Among these solutions are the call to strike, as seen in *Waiting for Lefty;* joining a socialistic or communistic society, as suggested by Sinclair in *The Jungle;* or finding a new set of values within an altered social and family situation, as suggested by Odets in *Paradise Lost.* The answers are not always convincing or even workable, but, as is pointed out in *The Readers' Encyclopedia,* edited by William Rose Benét: "To a large degree this type of literature represented the sincere response of its authors to an era of economic depression and unemployment and to certain persistent social injustices which they knew from their own experience or observation. . . . *Waiting for Lefty* and *Let Freedom Ring* are characteristic proletarian plays." The people seeing proletarian plays did not necessarily demand that the solutions to the problems presented be worked out in detail. They received satisfaction from knowing that the basic problems were being presented forcefully; and they somehow felt that, from the mere airing of the problems, solutions would come. If the solutions advanced by proletarian authors were not entirely feasible, at least attention was brought to the problem and, in the minds of many, the recognition of the problem was the first step towards amelioration of it.

II *Odets' Proletarianism*

It is abundantly clear that of Odets' first five plays, all are basically proletarian except *Till the Day I Die,* which is concerned with fascism and the persecution of Jews. In *The Cycle of American Literature,* Robert Spiller calls *Waiting for Lefty* and *Golden Boy* "specifically proletarian" and goes on to contend that such writers as Elmer Rice do not achieve the proletarian outlook so fully as Odets does. Odets, of course, was completely caught up in the dilemma of the middle class during the early Depression years, for, though his family was now in comfortable circumstances, the young playwright had to make his way in a very uncertain world. The social forces of his age, the strong call of workers to unite, the search for answers to social problems in socialistic and communistic political groups, did much to shape the young playwright's thinking. He felt a strong emotional bond with the working class, although his contact with this class was quite remote. It represented to him what his family had been, it recalled his childhood, it awakened in him a sense of nostalgia. He was not fundamentally a part of it; he could, however, observe it with sympathy, could even feel empathy with it. The warm compassion with which he could watch people in Stewart's Cafeteria or in run-down burlesque houses did not make him one with these people. He could remain objective towards them, hence he could forcefully portray a whole gallery of them in a play like *Waiting for Lefty*.

Odets and most of the proletarian writers of the 1930's looked upon their writing as something instrumental. They were not concerned with art for art's sake and, indeed, were willing to sacrifice artistic effect for a social effect if necessary. In some of the writing of this period, the social effect has been so strong that the artistic aims of the writer have been overlooked. It is only recently, for example, that Steinbeck's *The Grapes of Wrath* has been viewed by a critic as a serious work of conscious artistry.[1] Much of the criticism of the period was social rather than literary.

The proletarian writers were generally quite willing to admit that what they were writing was propaganda, designed to arouse audiences and to win support for specific causes. These artists wanted to write for and about their own times, and they had to forge ahead on their own as they found the old forms of literary expression failing them. They had to find new social metaphors through which to state their cases and make their points. Realizing the need for new forms, Odets developed a technique in *Waiting for Lefty* which was new to many American playgoers: he planted actors in the midst of the audience and had them enter the action of the play as they were needed. His technique of presenting brief, slice-of-life scenes was also novel in American drama. His technique basically was to involve the audience in the action of his play by the use of every device which he could contrive. The result was that in performances of *Waiting for Lefty* audiences felt sufficiently a part of the action to join in the call at the end of the play to "STRIKE, STRIKE, STRIKE!"

John Gassner, writing in 1949 in *Theatre Arts Monthly*, saw, a decade and a half after Odets first became prominent in American drama, what many critics had overlooked in Odets' work: "Odets has been a writer of allegories in all his work except the underground drama *Till the Day I Die*. . . . The allegorical method was an almost inevitable procedure for a man who sought significance for his narration, vents for explosiveness of his characters, and a function for his poetic and romantic flare [*sic*]." Mr Gassner continues, "Odets, who could never be content with mere realism . . . had to transfigure his particulars if he was to write at all." A statement such as this, if accepted as valid, gives a new dimension to Odets criticism specifically and, by extension, to the criticism of the proletarian movement of the 1930's. That Odets was consciously writing allegorically is clearly implied by the fact that an early draft of *Golden Boy* was designated, on the title page, "a modern allegory."[2] Hence, it would appear reasonable that in discussing the plays of Odets, especially in regard to their social and philosophical implications, one should consider both the surface meaning and the substrata of allegorical meaning which are present.

Odets very interestingly mingled extremes of realism with his allegory. He said that he could not ". . . see human life divorced from theme," and in this statement is a clue to what he was attempting to achieve artistically. He has had an overall, underlying theme which pervades all that he has written; in his own words, "All my plays . . . deal with one subject: the struggle not to have life nullified by circumstances, false values, anything." Odets made this statement in 1955, by which time all of his dramas discussed in this study had been written and produced. It is especially important that one who would understand his plays, from *Rocket to the Moon* to *The Flowering Peach*, bear in mind the author's conscious concern with this theme.

Odets' basic concern has been more with causes than with effects or with remedies. He views his obligation as a writer as being more social than artistic. He attempted to demonstrate his social protest when he went to Cuba in 1935, but he later realized that this was not the most effective way in which he could work towards altering those aspects of his society which he did not find agreeable to him. He came to realize after the Cuban debacle that he could more effectively advance his beliefs through writing than through leading active protest groups. In reference to this point, he said to an interviewer from *Time Magazine* in 1938: "People can do only one thing at a time. A writer must write. Besides, it is not the explosion which should most concern the artist,—it is the causes leading up to it." Certainly this has been true of most serious drama. When Nora slams the door in *A Doll's House,* the causes have been explored by Ibsen and have been presented to the audience. The effect of these causes is Nora's walking out, and with this the play ends. Similarly, the effect of Antigone's actions is that she dies and that Creon's family is destroyed; the causes are, to a degree, presented throughout the three plays of the Oedipus trilogy. For dramatic reasons, some plays, such as *Waiting for Lefty,* begin with the effect which a series of causes has led up to, but such plays are still ultimately concerned with causes which are explored through some sort of flashback technique.

During a decade when the proletariat was attempting to find an answer to the problems which the Depression inflicted upon it, Odets was aflame with indignation at the plight of men who had lost their self-respect and self-confidence. He transformed this indignation into a sound dramatic presentation in *Waiting for Lefty,* and later in such plays as *Awake and Sing!, Golden Boy,* and *Paradise Lost.* And while the angle of his vision was somewhat altered in such later productions as *The Country Girl* and *The Big Knife,* his concern was still with men who had lost self-respect and self-confidence and he was still desirous that lives should not be ". . . nullified by circumstances, false values."

Odets' indignation combined with his rich human compassion to gain him the support of people who did not share his views in any way. One critic noted that "he spoke of America, of its indestructible good nature." But more than this, he spoke from his deepest convictions with warmth, vitality, and sincerity, in the language of the people, bringing large audiences, ". . . blind to all sight and sound which they had . . . not measured with their own senses," to an understanding of what sort of tedious and perilous treadmill life was to those who were oppressed by it.

The people who saw such plays as *Waiting for Lefty* and *Awake and Sing!* were obviously not the people whose day-to-day existence was being jeopardized by the Depression. People who went to the theatre in the Depression era might be feeling the economic pinch of the Depression but they were not living the marginal existence of the "cabbies" in *Waiting for Lefty,* or a theatre ticket would have been beyond reach. Because the Group endeavored to present plays which contained material dealing honestly with American social life and problems and to present such plays to the widest possible audience, the organization attempted to keep the cost of the tickets low; however, even a fifty-cent ticket for *Waiting for Lefty* cost more than an unemployed worker could pay. Hence, the problems about which Odets was writing were often aired before people who were not so desperately in the grips of the Depression as were the characters in his plays. Perhaps this accounts in part for his enormous success in 1935: he had the moral support of the oppressed, and he gained the sympathy and understanding of those in better circumstances, who, while they were aware of effects which were evident about them, had often been only moderately aware of the causes. Odets presented the causes with enough force to cause Darien matrons and Scarsdale dowagers viewing matinee performances of *Waiting for Lefty* to rise at the end of the play and call "STRIKE, STRIKE, STRIKE!" as passionately as it might be called by a group of "cabbies" gathered in a union hall.

CHAPTER 3

The Early Plays

"The blood of the mother
and brother is breaking
upon my head . . .
Hungry men I hear."
(From *I Can't Sleep*)

FOR THE PURPOSES of this study, the early plays of Clifford Odets are construed as being those plays written before the author went to Hollywood for the first time. *Golden Boy*, the one exception, is included with this group because of its thematic similarity to the four other plays of the early period: *Waiting for Lefty, Awake and Sing!, Till the Day I Die*, and *Paradise Lost*.

The plays under consideration will be discussed in order of production, although this is, obviously, not the order of composition. Odets himself said in a letter to Marion Gallaway that it would be difficult to arrange his plays in order of any strict chronology.[1] It is known that *Awake and Sing* existed in an early draft before *Waiting for Lefty* was written, and that *Paradise Lost* was two-thirds written by the end of 1934.

Till the Day I Die does not entirely coincide thematically with the other plays of this early group; however, it is, in its indignation and verve, distinctly a part of the author's early period, and its concern with the interrelation of communist and fascist philosophies does shed light on the political feelings of Odets in a period pregnant with political protest. John Howard Lawson said that in *Till the Day I Die* Odets "projects a personal conflict,"[2] and it is clear that this personal conflict is very much a part of the other early plays.

Odets' social concepts emerge from these plays as he considers (1) man's relation to the state; (2) man's relation to his fellow man; (3) man's relation to his family; and (4) man's relation to himself. The last of these considerations, the question of how man is to maintain self-respect in the face of grave socio-economic problems, is vitally connected with the other considerations, but it is actually the central concern of most of Odets' writing.

I *Waiting for Lefty*

Waiting for Lefty[3] is undoubtedly the most angry play which Clifford Odets has ever had produced. In this play he uses the interesting technique of spotlighting individuals in the mass and of permitting the basic conflict to evolve through their separate stories; hence, in effect, each scene is a small play unto itself with its own development and climax, and each of these small plays contributes to the total play and to its climax. The original order of the scenes in *Waiting for Lefty* was as follows: Union Assembly Hall Scene; Joe and Edna; The Young Hack and His Girl; The Labor Spy Episode; The Young Actor; The Interne; The Agate Episode.[4] However, later versions of the play, including that which is reproduced in *Six Plays of Clifford Odets*, omitted the scene involving the actor and replaced it with the laboratory-assistant scene. The order was also changed so that between each scene involving a regular cab driver or a representative of the working class, there is a scene involving some professional person who has been led by circumstance to become a cab driver. Thus, the final order of scenes is as follows: Union Assembly Hall Scene; Joe and Edna; Laboratory Assistant; The Young Hack and His Girl; The Labor Spy Episode; The Interne; The Agate Episode. The scenes will be discussed in the revised rather than in the original order.

In the opening scene, Fatt, a union organizer and leader, is trying to dissuade the union membership from striking. But the membership is eager to strike and anxiously awaits the arrival of Lefty Costello who will support them in their eagerness. Tension mounts as a voice of agitation calls out from the audience that the whole country is "on the blink." The voice belongs to Joe, a veteran with shrapnel in his body, who calls himself one of the "black and blue" boys. As he begins to speak in favor of an immediate strike, the lights fade and a spotlight picks up a scene in which Joe and his wife, Edna, are talking. They are in their bare apartment and Joe has just been informed that the furniture has been taken away because he has not been able to meet the installment payments.

Joe is disheartened because his earnings as a taxicab driver amount to only six or seven dollars a week, scarcely enough to pay for any living expenses beyond rent. Edna, beset by the problem of how to meet the rent which will fall due the following day, looks at Joe peculiarly as he snaps:

> Don't look at me that way, Edna.
> EDNA: I'm looking through you, not at you. . . . You're
> a four-star-bust. . . . Who's the man in the family, you
> or me?   (8-9)

Joe, emasculated by the effects of continued poverty and defeat, is able to answer only: "Tell me what to do!" Obviously Joe is not the man of the house; he is not able to decide either his own destiny or that of his family. He can only retreat into a retrospective reverie which causes him to say, " I wish I was a kid again and didn't have to think about the next minute" (9). But Edna is stronger than Joe and will not permit him this meditative retreat; she demands action with the words, "For God's sake, do something, Joe, get wise. Maybe get your buddies together, maybe go on strike for better money." But Joe is not persuaded. He points out that strikes don't work and that during a strike no money is coming in. Joe is the little man caught in a trap between two encompassing walls of evil: on one side is the capitalist, using the little man as his pawn as he pursues his course towards greater wealth; on the other hand is the labor leader of whom Joe says, "You know they're racketeers. The guys at the top would shoot you for a nickel. . . . Don't you wanna see me alive?" (10). Edna thoughtfully replies, "No . . . I don't think I do, Joe. Not if you can lift a finger to do something about it, and don't."

Edna's comment, spoken not impetuously but thoughtfully, implies a breakdown of the basic family structure and a gap between husband and wife which becomes wider still when Edna announces that her way out of the dilemma is to begin seeing her old boyfriend again. She tells Joe, "I'd leave you like a shot!" (11), when he tries to reason with her. Edna tells Joe that he is slaving to make his boss rich and his boss is ". . . giving your kids that fancy disease called rickets. He's making a jellyfish outa you and putting wrinkles in my face." Joe retorts, ". . . you're talking like a Red," and Edna, most significantly, answers, "I don't know what that means. But when a man knocks you down you get up and kiss his fist!" (12).

In this statement is part of the crux of what Odets is saying: Edna does not know what it means to be a Red! The course which she suggests has not grown out of any allegiance to a given political philosophy, but is the only course to pursue against the bully, and the capitalist is clearly identified as the bully. Her statement earlier in the scene that ". . . the world is supposed to be for all of us," is again a Marxian statement, but one which few of those oppressed by the Depression would have disputed during the 1930's. The statement, coming as it does from Edna's lips, is dramatic and forceful simply because she is not speaking as an apologist for any political group; she is not a Red, she is not a revolutionary, she is not an agitator as such; she is merely a wife and mother who desires those necessities of life which will permit her children to grow into healthy adults. Her desire is universal; her solution, seemingly, is natural.

Joe now rises to action. The scene shifts again to the union hall, where Joe utters the words, "We gotta walk out!" and returns to his seat. He has found a short-term solution, one which might conceivably precipitate reform. Odets has not suggested more than a beginning towards the solution of the problem as it exists, but Joe is ready, at least to take action and to stand firm in the protection of his family's rights as well as his own. In this scene it is obvious that Odets realizes that the inner conflicts of the individual are caused by the social conflict; and it, in turn, is conditioned by the economic struggle. Anita Block has pointed out in *The Changing World in Plays and Theatre* that Odets ". . . interprets, therefore, even the most personal problems of his characters in the light of this social conditioning, thus placing himself . . . in the general category of *social* dramatist." As such he provides society with some hope and that hope is, as is obvious from the play's context, a type of communism spelled with a small "c."

The next scene is between Miller, the laboratory assistant, and Fayette, the industrialist. Miller is a taxi driver who has been fired from his former job as a research assistant because he has ideals which will not permit moral compromise. In this scene the audience is brought face-to-face with the capitalist in the person of a manufacturer of poison gas. Miller is about to receive a promotion to a new post which will require him to spy on Dr. Brenner, an eminent chemist.

Fayette, the industrialist, is a man who thrives on strife between nations. Miller, an idealist, has lost a brother in the war, as well as two cousins. Fayette tells him that "the world is an armed camp today. . . But Uncle Sam won't be caught napping" (15). Miller, speaking for the proletariat, muses distractedly, "They say 12 million men were killed in that last one and 20 million more wounded or missing." Fayette's answer, shocking in its brutality and frankness, is specifically intended to portray the typical captain of industry as he appears in the eyes of the proletariat: "That's not our worry. If big business went sentimental over human life there wouldn't be big business of any sort!" The descant is, "Remember, you're with a growing organization!"

Miller finally refuses to do Fayette's bidding, saying he would "Rather dig ditches first!" (16). Fayette replies, "That's a big job for foreigners" (17). Miller then expresses the sentiments of the audience by saying, "But sneaking—and making poison gas—that's for Americans?" Fayette, unruffled, asks, "No hard feelings?" and Miller, chafing from what he has just heard, strikes out with the last speech in the scene—"Sure hard feelings! I'm not the civilized type, Mr. Fayette. Nothing suave or sophisticated about me. Plenty of hard feelings. Enough to want to bust you and all your kind square in the mouth!" He does this, and the scene is blacked out.

Miller's basic concern here is with his relations to his fellow men. How can he, as a scientist, pursue a course of action which will lead to an undesirable end for mankind? How can he, as a man, degrade himself by spying on another scientist? How can he, for money and security, sell to the capitalist his own inner soul? His fist smashes through the chrysalis within which he is secure; with his gesture of punching Fayette's jaw, he frees himself as a human being. His gesture puts him out of a job at a time when jobs are very scarce; but, as Odets indicates in most of his plays, man must be able to make his living in such a way that his own ideals will not be compromised, and Miller's role is consistent with this philosophy. However, having left one job because he would not compromise, he is now trying to avoid compromise in yet another job by supporting the union in its claims against the taxi company. Odets would appear to be indicating that it is very difficult indeed for man to find a way to survive without sacrificing some of his idealism.

In the next scene, Odets is concerned with two young people in love. Sid is a hack driver whose girl, Florrie, lives with her mother and brother Irv. Irv is afraid that Florrie and Sid will marry, have children, and then turn to him for aid in supporting their offspring. He points up a very real problem of the Depression era when he tells his sister, "This ain't no time to get married. Maybe later—"; he follows this statement with, "Nowadays is no time to be soft. You gotta be hard as a rock or go under"5 (18).

Sid is basically an acceptable suitor for Florrie. Irv has no objection to him as a person; but he can see no future for the pair, who have been engaged to be married for three years in which time ". . . we never even had a room to sit in somewhere." This theme of homelessness is to recur and be much elucidated in *Night Music*, and elements of it are apparent in *Till the Day I Die* and in *Paradise Lost*.6

Sid is convinced that ". . . the cards is stacked for all of us. The money man is dealing himself a hot royal flush. Then giving you and me a phony hand like a pair of tens or something. . . . Then he says, what's the matter you can't win—no stuff on the ball, he says to you." He finally concludes: "If we can't climb higher than this together—we better stay apart—We got the blues, Babe—the 1935 blues" (21-22). The problem here is clearly an economic one for which there seems no immediate solution. A strike might conceivably offer hope. Sid and Florrie have nothing to lose by a strike, for their situation cannot be much worse than it now is. Odets presents them as lovable, sympathetic characters; characters caught in a vise between grasping labor leaders and avaricious capitalists lacking a social conscience. These forces are closing in upon them to rob them of the happiness of their youth and of the natural fulfillment which life might be expected to hold. Overall political concepts do not concern Sid and Florrie; they are aware only of the dimensions of their own problem; and if the solution involves the acceptance of a political doctrine at loggerheads with the system of free enterprise, they are not in a position to question it or to probe into the implications of it from a very long-term point of view. Odets is illustrating that desperate men cannot see very far beyond the solution of their own immediate problems. Hence, by extension, a nation composed of desperate men can enjoy little stability. As a result, the interrelation of the workers, the capitalists, and the government is clearly delineated in Odets' mind and becomes implicit in what is said in this scene.

Scene IV is essentially an exposé of the role of the labor spy in union activities. Clayton, the spy, is uncovered by one of the taxicab drivers in the audience. Fatt wields his power by saying to the accuser, "You'll prove all this or I'll bust you in every hack outfit in town!" (24). The dispute continues until the voice in the audience says in anguish, "He's my own lousy brother" (25). This scene, although not notable for making the play more organic, is used effectively to emphasize the climate of distrust which oppresses the worker from every side at a time of crisis. It also points out that those who are apparently union supporters and sympathizers might very well be unworthy of the trust of the union membership and might represent a very real threat to the people with whom they seemingly ally themselves.

Probably the person least expected to be found driving a taxi is Dr. Benjamin, whose story is told in Scene V. He has had a hospital residency and has gained seniority at his hospital, an institution which deals chiefly with charity cases. His immediate superior and very close personal friend is Dr. Barnes, a non-Jew with whom Benjamin, a Jew, has always felt on equal terms as a person. Naturally, when Benjamin is informed that he is to be dismissed from the hospital staff, he turns to Dr. Barnes for an explanation. Barnes hints darkly that anti-Semitism is the pretext for Benjamin's dismissal. Benjamin is to be replaced in the operating room by Dr. Leeds who is ". . . incompetent as hell." Dr. Barnes, who realizes that this is the case, reminds Dr. Benjamin that "Doctors don't run hospitals" (26). Leeds is the nephew of Senator Leeds and his incompetence does not prevent him from succeeding in his profession.

Benjamin is astounded by his dismissal, especially in view of the fact that there are ". . . all those wealthy brother Jews on the board" (27). But Dr. Barnes, in his years at the hospital, has observed that there ". . . doesn't seem to be much difference between wealthy Jews and rich Gentiles. Cut from the same piece!" (28). In this statement, of course, Odets is venting his feelings about those who succeed in the capitalistic system: apparently the acquisition of wealth has ruined them and has sapped them of their humanity.

One solution occurs to Benjamin as a feasible means of overcoming his situation: he might go to Russia, because ". . . in a rich man's country your true self's buried deep . . . you don't believe theories until they happen to you" (28). This last point is wholly consistent with what has been said earlier in the play, and it emphasizes the underlying political philosophy of the entire drama. Practically every problem is reducible to economic factors, and solutions are to be found in an economically egalitarian system of government.

It is significant that Dr. Benjamin did not go to Russia; here again Odets is suggesting that one must work within his own society to bring about reform rather than flee to a society in which the desired reform has already been brought about. Dr. Benjamin, after he decides to stay in the United States, says: "Our work's here—America! I'm scared . . . What future's ahead, I don't know. Get some job to keep alive—maybe drive a cab—and study and work to learn my place—. . . Fight! Maybe get killed, but goddamn! We'll go ahead!" (28-29). When Dr. Benjamin speaks of learning his place, he is not implying that he is going to learn subservience. He is concerned with learning the place of man in universal terms; he is concerned with knowing the details of the social contract which is imposed upon man at birth.

Scene V is very important to the play. In the first place, it is the only scene in the play which brings up the problem of anti-Semitism, a problem which was very apparent during the 1930's and a problem which very strongly influenced hiring policies during this era. Secondly, the line that "doctors don't run hospitals" is telling both in its truth and in its relation to the situation in which the cab drivers find themselves. They are trying to join in a concerted effort so that they, the people most affected by the workings of their company, will have some voice in what the company's policy shall be. The company is opposed to this. But a parallel, and a rather shocking one since it involves a situation directly involved with human life, is found in the conducting of a hospital. Indeed, Dr. Barnes makes his statement in more general terms when he says: "Doctors don't run medicine in this country. The men who know their jobs don't run anything here, except the motormen on trolley cars" (27-28). This sentiment, while not entirely valid, and certainly, in the general terms in which Dr. Barnes states it, not supported, had received widespread acceptance in the 1930's, and one must always bear in mind that Odets is often repeating widespread sentiments which, if they are repeated often enough, become truth in the minds of those who are repeatedly exposed to them.

As the play enters its last scene, Agate rises and directs a barrage of criticism about the union at Fatt. But by this time the other members are aroused and Fatt's calls to order go unheeded as Agate makes his complaint. He rants: "This is your life and mine! It's skull and bones every incha the road! Christ, we're dying by inches! For what? For the debutant-ees to have their sweet comin' out parties in the Ritz! Poppa's got a daughter—she's gotta get her picture in the papers. Christ, they make 'em with our blood. Joe said it. Slow death or fight. It's war!" (30).

A high pitch of emotion is reached as Agate says, ". . . the man who got me food in 1932, he called me Comrade! The one who picked me up where I bled—he called me Comrade too! What are we waiting for. . . . Don't wait for Lefty! He might never come" (31). At this point a man enters and announces that Lefty has been found with a bullet through his head. The response is tumultuous:

> AGATE: Hear it, boys, hear it? Hell, listen to me! Coast to coast! HELLO AMERICA! HELLO. WE'RE STORM-BIRDS OF THE WORKING-CLASS. WORKERS OF THE WORLD. . . . OUR BONES AND BLOOD! And when we die they'll know what we did to make a new world! . . . Well, what's the answer?
> ALL: STRIKE!
> AGATE: LOUDER!
> ALL: STRIKE!
> AGATE AND OTHERS: AGAIN!
> ALL: STRIKE, STRIKE, STRIKE!

(31)

And thus ended the *tour de force* which first brought fame to Clifford Odets. The original version did not have quite the balance which was achieved by dropping the Young Actor Scene and replacing it with the Laboratory Assistant Scene. As has been mentioned, the order of scenes which was later adopted tends to juxtapose various segments of society with a more dramatic and contrasting effect than is found in the original order.

The Young Actor Scene is not unlike the others in basic outlook. The producer is portrayed as a gross creature, unfeeling, luxurious. His secretary is a Communist, filled with human compassion. She tells the young actor about the *Communist Manifesto* and about the hope which is offered to the oppressed through it and through the Communist Party. The scene suffers from superficial thinking on the part of the author, as well as from a tendency to oversimplify the solutions to problems which are essentially very complex. Actually, this criticism might be leveled at the play as a whole, but in the scene which Odets dropped, the oversimplification is a distinct weakness.

In the course of the Young Actor Scene, the stenographer mentions that the producer's Russian wolfhound, a rather ineffectual symbol of the worker, has just been gelded presumably at the insistence of the producer, the representative of the capitalist. Then she says to the young actor, "They do the same to you, but you don't know it." Again this is a consideration of what society is doing to the worker, to the bulk of healthy American manhood.

In *Waiting for Lefty,* despite its faults, there is a merging of symbol and fact; so complete is the merging that to many the play did not appear to have symbolic significance. However, it is obvious that the taxi strike became synonymous with the overthrow of economic exploitation of the masses and with the downfall of labor bosses, of poison gas manufacturing, of racial and religious discrimination, and of an over-all condition of unemployment. The product of the widespread discontent was a class-conscious working class, its forces augmented by the oppressed members of the professions.

Waiting for Lefty has not been acclaimed great literature. In the *Literary History of the United States,* Joseph Wood Krutch calls the play ingenious and forthright, but he points out that the "characterization is in simple black and white, much of the didacticism is crude as well as blatant." Krutch does go on to call the play effective as a weapon. Certainly the effects of the play were immediate and the appeal was enormous.

It seems abundantly clear that *Waiting for Lefty* is, as Brooks Atkinson noted in his review of the play, "fiercely dramatic in the theatre." The sympathetic characters are, on the whole, convincingly drawn, even though the less sympathetic ones are mere caricatures. John Howard Lawson has pointed out quite validly that the characters in *Waiting for Lefty* can hardly be called "stormbirds of the working class," but are, more accurately, "declassed members of the middle class." Lawson also notes that "it is assumed that the social forces which create the decision [in the scenes of the play] are absolute, and that the intuitive recognition of these forces is a moment of supreme climax. Thus the moment of clash, of the break between cause and effect, is neglected."[7]

It is difficult to discuss *Waiting for Lefty* in terms of structure, for it develops in such a way that the customary devices used to develop a play structurally are not necessary. In the traditional sense, the play might be said to be lacking in progression, as Lawson has mentioned; however, the progression within each scene is traditional. In discussing the entire play in terms of this element, one must realize that Lawson's sequence of events which constitutes progression—the decision, the grappling with difficulties, the test of strength, and the climax—is somewhat distorted in the Odets play. The chronology is also distorted because of the flashbacks. Hence, in the Joe and Edna scene, for example, the progression is completed in a relatively normal way, but in the next scene it begins over again. Often, also, the decision and the climax occur with approximate simultaneity.

Nevertheless, the action of the play is constantly forcing the inevitable outcome. The forward motion is rapid and direct, pressing dynamically towards a single philosophical point. The audience, drawn into the play almost immediately, finds it easy to identify itself with the various characters on stage. This, as Albert Hunt has recently mentioned in an article about Odets appearing in *Encore*, is partly because Odets uses the appeal of youth in his plays: "*Lefty* is ostensibly about a taxi drivers' strike, but three out of the six episodes deal with young intellectuals—an actor, a scientist, and a doctor—while a fourth is about young love. Odets' young people long for life to be beautiful, but at every turn they are confronted by corruption."[8] This striving of worthy young people, which had an immense appeal, pointed to the most serious evil of the Depression—the utter frustration of an upcoming generation unable to find any sort of security or fulfillment. As H. G. Wells has noted, for example, in *Homo Sapiens*, this sort of situation led in part to the rise of the Nazis in Germany.

The ideological core of *Waiting for Lefty* is essentially economic. The economic strife of the Depression is the uniting force which causes the participants in the action of the play to work towards the sort of social equality which they hope ultimately to attain. Hunt points out that *Waiting for Lefty* is as much reaction against the 1920's as against the 1930's. He writes that suddenly the 1920's were all over and "Instead of the jag, the breadline, and instead of the 'cosmic despair,' [one was faced with] Odets' 'We don't want life printed on dollar bills.'" The two decades, thrown into sharp contrast, contain both the causes and effects of the social dilemma with which Odets is so immensely concerned.

Capitalistic society is portrayed as a perverse force standing between the masses and ultimate fulfillment. Edna cries, "the world is supposed to be for all of us," and to an economically oppressed generation the statement sounds reasonable; however, closer scrutiny would quickly reveal what an oversimplification such a statement is. Odets returns again and again to the idea that man cannot have self-respect unless he has a voice in his own destiny, and that man without self-respect does not deserve to be called a *man*. In *Waiting for Lefty*, Odets is a righteously indignant man, speaking in his most stentorian tones, writing an angry social document, the product of youth and vigor. The play is one-sided in its outlook and is often questionable in terms of its logic; but in 1935 it spoke with a force which few playwrights have ever been able to attain and which Odets, as he became more artistically aware, was never to attain again.

II *Awake and Sing!*

The basic social unit with which Odets deals in *Awake and Sing!* is the family. He has been quoted as saying that the family is "society's basic biological cell . . . strong and organic." The Bergers, who represent in many ways a typical American family of the 1930's, are of the working class and are struggling to rise above this status. Ralph, the idealistic son, is just ". . . looking for a chance to get to first base," as is the rest of the family. But the play leaves one wondering whether in a capitalistic system, the sensitive and intelligent youth, Ralph, will ever be able to succeed.

The signs of success presented in the play in the persons of Uncle Morty and Moe Axelrod are not encouraging. Uncle Morty, a clothing manufacturer, has flouted labor's cause, "has risen out of its ranks to exploit it. Morty is a sensualist. He lives well, drives a big car and contributes the sum of five dollars a week toward the support of his father whom he baits as a 'nut.' "[9] Uncle Morty is insulated against any tender emotions which might tend to weaken him in his business dealings. We are told in the description of characters which is given before the play that "something sinister comes out of the fact that the lives of others seldom touch him deeply" (38). His philosophy is well summed up in his words, "In the long run common sense is thicker than love" (65). Though successful, Morty is a victim of the capitalistic system which, in the view of the play, deprives a man of all personality. He recognizes this lack in himself when he says, "Business don't stop for personal life" (89), but there is little he can do to remedy his situation; and it is unlikely that he would choose to remedy it if it were in his power to do so.

The other financially successful figure in the play is the embittered Moe Axelrod, a boarder in the Berger household, who lost one leg in the war and who, because of this injury, has the security of a government pension. A petty racketeer, his realistic view of life is: "It's all a racket—from horse racing on down. Marriage, politics, big business—everybody plays cops and robbers" (71). Moe is another product of a world order in which war is condoned as well as what Anita Block in *The Changing World in Plays and Theatre* calls the oppression and contrived insecurity of the worker.

It is important to note that both of the successful characters in this play are deformed: one, spiritually and emotionally; the other, physically and emotionally. If one is to accept Albert Hunt's theory that Odets deals entirely in symbols,[10] and this writer has a great inclination to do so, then Uncle Morty and Moe represent the compromise which one must make in order to succeed in a capitalistic system. Each is warped and crippled in his own way; each has made the adjustment within himself which success demands.

Ralph and Hennie represent the younger generation in the Berger household. Theirs is ". . . the struggle of the younger generation to get away from the sordid realities created by their parents, which bind them hand and foot," as Miss Block points out. But in winning their own struggle, they create for the succeeding generation sordid realities which, in the moral code of their society, are far more difficult to face than those created for them by their parents. When Hennie runs off with Moe Axelrod, leaving her husband and her child, she is creating a situation for that child which is essentially much less favorable than any which she ever had to face in her childhood. Anyone reading the play knows just how unfavorable a situation Hennie's child is left in because Odets, in the character descriptions before the play, says of a minor character, Schlosser, that he "is an overworked German whose wife ran away with another man and left him with a young daughter who in turn ran away and joined a burlesque show as chorus girl. The man suffers rheumatic pains. He has lost his identity twenty years before" (30). This description of a character who has only three small speeches in the play is indefensibly prolix unless it has some additional relationship to the play. The purpose of it is to point to the sort of situation which Hennie is creating for her child and husband.

In a way Hennie has actually had a much pleasanter existence than a girl in her circumstances might be expected to have. Bessie Berger, her mother, has had a sincere concern for her family, albeit an overconcern. But Bessie was ". . . not only the mother, but also the father. The first two years [of my marriage]," she says, "I worked in a stocking factory for six dollars a week while Myron Berger went to law school. If I didn't worry about the family who would?" (95). There is nothing of the dreamer about Bessie; her concern is with the here and now; her fundamental quest is respectability. When she admonishes her father, who is giving Uncle Morty a haircut, not to get any hair on the floor because "I like my house to look respectable" (59), it is obvious that she is stating the aim of her whole life. By the time she utters this statement, she has shown that her desire for respectability is the chief motivating force in her life, for she has already forced the pregnant Hennie into a marriage with a man whom Hennie does not love; Bessie does this in order to save face for the family, little realizing that she is forcing upon the family the ultimate deterioration which is evident at the close of the play. When Ralph discovers what his mother has done, he is completely appalled; he is even more shocked by the indifference of Jacob, his grandfather, who is an idealist and a Marxian, for having permitted Hennie to marry Sam Feinschreiber, who is to be deluded into thinking that Hennie's child is also his child. Ralph says to Jacob:

> I suppose you knew about this, Jake?
> JACOB: Yes.
> RALPH: Why didn't yo do something?

JACOB: I'm an old man.
RALPH: What's that got to do wth the price of bonds?
Sits around and lets a thing like that happen! You make
me sick too.

(84)

In these few lines it is evident that the older idealist, Jacob,
is not a man of action. He can only say, "This is a house?
Marx said it—abolish such families" (55), but he cannot rise
to action and he realizes this shortcoming in himself; indeed,
it is very largely this realization which leads to his suicide. He
is aware of the fact that his life has been a waste; his hope for
the future is in Ralph and he gives him advice which he has
never been able to follow himself: "This . . . I tell you—DO!
Do what is in your heart and carry in yourself a revolution.
But you should act. Not like me. A man who had golden oppor-
tunities but drank instead a glass tea" (78). This advice, of
course, suggests a solution to social ills which is so generalized,
so vague and tenuous, that it is really not a solution at all.

After Jacob has spoken his words of counsel, there is a pause
during which the mail plane from Boston flies above the house.
The mail plane is very much connected with the depiction of
Ralph's psychological constitution. It represents a vague, an-
ticipatory hope analogous to the dreamy hope in Ralph's lines
at the beginning of Act II which read, "When I was a kid I
laid awake at nights and heard the sounds of trains . . . far-
away lonesome sounds . . . boats going up and down the river.
I used to think of all kinds of things I wanted to do." Implicit
in the transportation theme is the sense of going somewhere
and to Ralph it is a sort of wish fulfillment; Ralph wants to
think that he is going somewhere, that he is accomplishing
something, that life has meaning and that *his* life specifically
will be meaningful.

The mail plane is also to recur as a *leit motif* when the
meaning of Jacob's life and thought finally becomes clear to
Ralph in the last act:

RALPH: I see every house lousy with lies and hate. He
said it, Grandpa—Brooklyn hates the Bronx. Smacked on the
nose twice a day. But boys and girls can get ahead like that,
Mom. We don't want life printed on dollar bills, Mom!

[58]

> BESSIE: So go out and change the world if you don't
> like it.
> RALPH: I will! And why? 'Cause life's different in my
> head. Gimme earth in two hands, I'm strong. There . . .
> hear him? The air mail off to Boston. Day or night, he flies
> away, a job to do. That's us and it's no time to die.
>
>   (95)

Whereas, just days before, Ralph had belittled his grandfather's statement that "never a young man had such opportunity like today. He could make history" (76), he now gives
his approval to it. He realizes the importance of action; and
in this speech as well as in his aforementioned speech at the
beginning of Act II, the accent is on the word "do." And this
word, of course, is the essence of Jacob's advice to Ralph.
Through his grandfather's death, Ralph has been reborn. Moe
Axelrod had said, in the last minutes of the play, ". . . cut off
your leg to save your life! And they done it—one thing to get
another." Now this statement echoes as Ralph vows, "My days
won't be for nothing. . . . I'm twenty-two and kickin'! I'll get
along. Did Jake die for us to fight about nickels? No! 'Awake
and sing,' he said. Right here he stood and said it. The night
he died, I saw it like a thunderbolt! I saw he was dead and I
was born! I swear to God, I'm one week old!" (100).

This speech is most dramatic, but it appeals more effectively
to one's sense of drama than to one's logic. As John Howard
Lawson points out, the audience is merely *told* that Ralph has
undergone a change. The change is not effectively or convincingly presented through any development in his character as
the play progresses. Essentially Ralph is left at the end of the
play with the same situation that faced him at the beginning
of it—with one exception: He has had the chance to change the
situation and did not.

At any rate, Moe Axelrod's statement, "One thing to get another," sums up much of Odets' philosophy here; the suicide
of Jake, who was constitutionally unable to rise to social action,
Odets would have his audience believe, has precipitated the
rebirth of a man who could rise to such action. Jake's hope had
always been in the future; he had used the past only in order
to be sure that he was building towards a better future, as

Ralph implies he will do when he comes to Jake's room with an armful of the old man's books. One cannot be sure that Ralph will be any more successful in attaining his ends than Jacob was, because Odets does not give one evidence that Ralph is a man of action, but rather suggests the contrary; he has shown some signs of being willing to rebel, but he demonstrates an inability to rebel in a situation so commonplace as that involving his relationship with Blanche, the young woman with whom he has fallen in love. He does appear to strike out against his mother when she tries to come between him and Blanche, and his speech in this regard is stirring, but he does not follow it up with action. He says to Bessie:

> I been working for years, bringing in money here—putting it in your hand like a kid. All right, I can't get my teeth fixed. All right, that a new suit's like trying to buy the Chrysler Building. You never in your life bought me a pair of skates even—things I died for when I was a kid. I don't care about that stuff, see. Only just remember I pay some of the bills around here, just a few . . . and if my girl calls me on the phone I'll talk to her any time I please.
>
> (66)

But when Blanche most needs Ralph's help, he does not give it. He hesitates to go to take her away from her unsympathetic uncle merely because he knows that her uncle is muscular and he doubts his own physical strength. Finally, when he has within his reach the legacy which Jacob has left him and when he might finally marry Blanche, he finds excuses and says to Moe, "No girl means anything to me until . . . I can take care of her. Till we don't look out on an airshaft. Till we can take the world in two hands and polish off the dirt" (96).

Hennie, as well as Ralph and Jacob, tends to live in the future; but she envisions a future of escape to a land of heart's desire as described to her by Moe, a place ". . . where it's moonlight and roses. We'll lay down, count stars. Hear the big ocean making noise. You lay under the trees. Champagne flows like——" (98). But Hennie is the antithesis of Ralph and Jacob, for to them it is important that "life should have some dignity," while to Hennie this is unimportant. She wants to be comfortable physically and materially. Jacob has always stressed the value of love, but Hennie is incapable of loving either her husband or her child. She would willingly leave them in order to find an easier life with Moe, a man whom she does not love either.

This presentation of Hennie has caused many people to level unfavorable criticism at Odets' values; however, it seems evident that he is diagnosing one of the major ills of society; he is stressing the fact that circumstances can completely nullify one's ability to love and that Hennie's behavior is inevitable in the light of the circumstances which have been so much a factor in the development of her personality. Hennie lacks understanding and is utterly unable to face life realistically. Romance has replaced reason in her. She has utterly no understanding of or interest in the ideological positions of Ralph and Jacob; she cannot strive towards the new world which they envisage, so she strives towards the only hopeful goal within her reach. The point of Hennie's action is only that of emphasizing the moral chaos which Odets saw about him as a result of the Depression and, by extension, of the capitalistic system.

Hennie would agree with Uncle Morty that "to raise a family nowadays you must be a damn fool." This sentiment, already seen in *Waiting for Lefty,* is the sentiment of an age, and Uncle Morty is Odets' representation of the practical capitalist. However, Uncle Morty's statement does not go unchallenged, for Bessie Berger, speaking for her particular segment of Jewish society, answers, ". . . a woman who don't raise a family—a girl—should jump overboard. What's she good for?" (62). Bessie represents nothing so fully in the play as she does stolid plodding and continuance. She lives from day to day; but through the most trying situations Bessie continues to maintain her family. Hennie expresses what the audience comes to feel about Bessie when she says of her mother, "She'll go on forever" (100).

Bessie is fully aware that the margin between having a home and some degree of security and family stability and not having these things is very narrow. More than once she refers to people who have been evicted from their homes and this thought is nightmarish to her: "They threw out a family on Dawson Street today. All the furniture on the sidewalk. A fine old woman with gray hair" (43). This is the sort of situation with which Bessie feels an extreme empathy, especially in view of her emphasis on maintaining a front of respectability. If Bessie has dominated her family to such a point that her husband has lost all semblance of self-respect and her children find her hard to bear, she has done so in order to preserve the family as a physical unit. She cannot agree with Jake that family should be abolished any more than she can agree with Uncle Morty that "to raise a family nowadays you must be a damn fool." Bessie, despite all of the problems which the family causes her, enjoys her role of mother which she has turned into the role of martyr.

Myron, her husband, has been a clerk for thirty years. He has never known success, but he cannot entirely admit defeat either. He lives almost exclusively in the past, nurturing his hero worship for Theodore Roosevelt, a man who stands in polar opposition to him temperamentally. Myron's gullibility makes him blind to the social injustices which trouble Ralph and Jacob. Myron has yearned for success, but he does not realize that "all the cards of the social structure . . . were stacked against him."[11] Instead of despairing, he puts fifty cents into the Irish Sweepstakes and hopes for sudden, dramatic success; or he bets on a horse, winning just often enough so that he does not lose hope and will continue to place his bets regularly; or he enters a contest to name a beauty who is going on the air to advertise cosmetics. When Moe says that Myron still believes in Santa Claus, Myron answers with naive faith, "Someone's got to win. The government isn't gonna allow everything to be a fake" (87).

This is perhaps the most telling statement that Myron makes in the entire course of the play. It reveals what his life has been—a fake. The sum total of his existence adds up to zero; he has grown so used to frustration that he accepts it as commonplace in his life. Only a miracle can alter Myron's existence, so there is no reason for him not to believe in miracles. Without this hope, life would be utterly meaningless and hopeless to him. Petty gambling, in his life, fills the need which Marxism fills in the lives of Jake and Ralph. All three are basically interested in materialistic betterment in life: Myron, on an individual basis; Ralph and Jake on a level which would affect all of society. But, despite Ralph's philosophical solution to the ills of society, one cannot help comparing his statement, "I pay some of the bills around here" (66), with Uncle Morty's statement to Jake that ". . . without rich men around you don't have a roof over your head" (72). Both men, despite the extreme cultural and philosophical gap between them, are using a baldly economic standard as a means of self-assertion.

It is obvious that Odets is concerned in this play with what he calls "general fraud." This he defined in an interview for *Time Magazine* as ". . . the Cinderella approach to life, the American success story." It is because of his concern with "general fraud" that he emphasizes Hennie's interest in the movies; it is her one easily obtainable means of escape. This theme of basing one's dreams on Hollywood standards is recurrent in the play and is blasted by Jake, who, instead, dreams of something which he feels is within the reach of the masses. In talking about "success," Jake says that American youth dreams all night of fortunes: "Why not? Don't it say in the movies he should have a personal steamship, pyjamas [*sic*] for fifty dollars a pair and a toilet like a monument? But in the morning he wakes up and for ten dollars he can't fix the teeth. And millions are worse off" (71-72). It is with such juxtapositions that Odets achieves his highest level of social dynamism. This, to Odets, is the great American lie. This is the sort of thing to which Ralph refers when he says, "I see every house lousy with lies and hate" (95). The lies spawn the hatred which grows from ". . . the persistent and many-sided rebellion of human nature against everything which thwarts it," as Joseph Wood Krutch points out in *The American Drama Since 1918.*

The only real point of communication between the various members of the Berger family is that each wants something desperately and that each is thwarted in his quest. The family, dominated by Bessie, becomes an instrument of unjust coercion; its boredom leads Hennie to have an affair which results in her pregnancy. Bessie, more vitally concerned with respectability than with the ultimate good of her daughter, arranges a marriage which cannot succeed in doing anything more than giving legitimacy to an unborn child. She does all this because she is so sensitive to the pressures of public opinion, because she is weighed down by what Odets considers to be a set of obsolete social values. The effect of this marriage is far-reaching: Not only is Hennie to find herself in a situation which she cannot endure, but Jake and Ralph are completely nonplused by the basic immorality of what Bessie has done to Hennie and to the likeable, naïve Sam Feinschreiber.

There is little fully developed situation in the plot of *Awake and Sing!* The play is sustained primarily through character development, and the characters, with the possible exception of Jake and Ralph, are examples of people with a great spiritual lack. This deficiency is sharpened, as Edith Isaacs noted in *Theatre Arts Monthly*, "by an immediate economic crisis, which has made them morbid, frustrated, decadent." Odets is writing from the inside out; he is able to do so because he is emotionally akin to the people about whom he is writing.

If there is anything recognizable as hope in the conclusion of *Awake and Sing!*, it is hope with a bitter aftertaste. As the play reaches its end, Ralph urges Hennie to go off with Moe: ". . . do it, Hennie, do it!" he exhorts her. This is Ralph calling for action, but he wants this action merely for its own sake, not because it represents any overall good. He is urging her on towards a course which is totally irresponsible and unrealistic. What happens to Hennie just before the conclusion of the play is almost a metaphorical commentary on what happens to mankind in the social situation. Moe asks Hennie to go off with him:

HENNIE: Leave the baby?
MOE: Yeah!
HENNIE: I can't . . .
MOE: You can!
HENNIE: No . . .
MOE: But you're not sure!
HENNIE: I don't know.
MOE: Make a break or spend the rest of your life in a coffin.
HENNIE: Oh God, I don't know where I stand.
MOE: Don't look up there. Paradise, you're on a big boat headed south . . . and when you cry it's because you're happy.
HENNIE: Moe, I don't know . . .

MOE: Nobody knows, but you do it and find out. When you're scared the answer's zero.

HENNIE: You're hurting my arm.

(99-100)

And with this Hennie capitulates. This has been Hennie's whole life: capitulation, compromise, uncertainty, regret. Circumstances have been "hurting her arm" for as long as she can remember, and she has had no control over this.

Myron, as the play concludes, brings out with poignancy another bit of grim irony which has from time to time run through the action. Early in the play Moe rants because there is not an orange in the house, just an apple. And in the last moments of action Myron says, "No fruit in the house lately. Just a lone apple" (100). This, of course, serves to emphasize once more the utter lack of luxuries in the Berger household. But it goes beyond that to suggest rather dismally what man's future might be. Continuance and endless recurrence are the fruits of man's frailty as it is depicted in the Judeo-Christian concepts of the creation of man. Myron goes off paring his apple as Ralph says, "When I look at him, I'm sad. Let me die like a dog, if I can't get more from life" (100). The looming question is whether Ralph and succeeding generations *will* get more from life. There is no overwhelming call to action as at the conclusion of *Waiting for Lefty*. Rather, the audience is left with a very faint hope and with the thought that the play's title must be ironic. The decision of what man's destiny will be is placed in the hands of an audience left pondering, not shouting.

III *Till the Day I Die*

Till the Day I Die was one of the first serious anti-Nazi plays to be seen in New York, and is the first one to concentrate on the plight of the German Communists rather than on the persecution of the Jews.

The course of Marxism in Hitler's Germany is an interesting one. In *Studies in Sociology*, Morris Ginsberg states that class consciousness generally ". . . consists of a feeling of equality in relation to the members of one's own class, of inferiority in relation to those above in the hierarchy, and of superiority in relation to those below." Marxism in Germany, as elsewhere, greatly strengthened the feeling of equality and transformed the feeling of absolute inferiority of a class at the bottom of the social ladder into one of absolute superiority, for th's class was henceforth confident that it would supersede all other existing classes. Marxism, then, appealed to the craving for status and for property. Eva Reichmann, in *Hostages of Civilisation,* wrote that the Marxists told the people, "You are poor. . . . But in this capitalistic system your poverty is an intrinsic necessity, and at the same time the essential preliminary to a revolution which will bring about your triumph." This was, essentially, the feeling of the not inconsiderable number of Communists in Germany during the Hitler regime. This was a time when it was difficult for the average man to manage economically, even though unemployment had decreased. Part of the problem is stated in *Till the Day I Die* by Ernst Tausig, who says that ". . . workers might like to know the American embargo on German goods has increased 50% in the last six months. They might like to know wages are down one-third and vital foods are up seventy-five per cent" (107).

At the heart of the play is the author's concern with the question of the effect of oppression on the human being, on his society, and on the oppressors. The victim in the play is Ernst Tausig, a conscientious party member, a lover of music, a violinist before these days of brutality. His fingers are now stiff. "Not to have touched a violin in six months? Incredible!" he laments (108). Ernst, not particularly a revolutionary type, has been forced by circumstances into his present situation. He doesn't like it, but there is little he can do to alter it. He has had a long struggle within himself, and the play focuses on the final phases of the struggle which has been going on for years.

The threatening evil of fascism has pressed Ernst into revolutionary action, as it has his brother Carl, his mistress Tilly, and his friend Baum who ". . . used to be a peaceful man who planted tulips" (108). Carl expresses the aspirations of the typical party member when he explains that he walks down the street singing in order to throw the Nazis off guard and ". . . they don't know I'm singing because I know where we'll be some day" (109). This sentiment echoes throughout the play right down to the end when Ernst, about to take his own life, says, "The day is coming and I'll be in the final result. . . . Tilly, Carl, our agony is real. But we live in the joy of a great coming people! The animal kingdom is past. . . . Yes, a world of security and freedom is waiting for all mankind" (153-54). This is the end toward which Ernst and his party are working in the face of an almost overwhelming opposition. Ernst's hope is in his child, soon to be borne by Tilly.

Ernst and his comrades live in a climate of tension and distrust. The tension is heightened dramatically when, at the conclusion of each scene, "a half dozen whistles, variously pitched [are sounded], slowing with hysterical intensity" (113). The effect is pervasive, as is the increasing effect of distrust as the play proceeds. In the beginning, every knock on the door creates an inner panic; but as the play continues, the distrust is more subtly portrayed. No one is sure of anyone's loyalties. When Ernst is taken to the Columbia Brown House for interrogation by the Gestapo, a "trooper passes through, whispers 'Courage' to Ernst" (115). And when Ernst is questioned by Major Duhring just prior to his first release from custody, he discovers that the major, a former Communist who has not abandoned his former ideals, still looks upon himself as loyal to the Communists. Duhring, just before his suicide, cries out, "In every capitalist country in the world this day let them work for the united front" (135).

Just as the Nazi ranks are infiltrated by Communists, so are the Communist ranks infiltrated by Nazis. Each group therefore is concerned about the loyalty of its own membership. The Nazis build on this distrust and force Communist prisoners to accompany them on raids and to stand about, very well-dressed, outside the courtrooms in which their compatriots are being tried for their various activities. The Nazis go so far as to print leaflets under the imprimatur of underground organizations. Ernst makes this clear when he says, ". . . the first leaflet appears: 'Ernst Tausig is a paid stool pigeon.' Who printed them? Comrades? No, the Nazis" (152).

The terms in which the Nazis are described leave little room for doubt that they are all villains—a group of sadistic brutes who amuse themselves by seeing which of them can knock prisoners unconscious with a single blow. Their ranks are riddled with moral degenerates such as Schlegel and Adolph in

Scene II. The Nazis spy on each other and engage in black-mail, but the Communists' ranks are depicted as being much more unified and well organized. Despite this portrayal, the audience is asked to believe that the Communist underground is not sufficiently cognizant of Nazi tactics to realize what is being done to Ernst and why. Instead of extolling his heroism, the party places Ernst's name on the blacklist. Carl, Ernst's own brother, shows himself to be the true Communist when, after reminiscing about the childhood which he and his bro-ther had known together, he says: "It is brother against brother. Many a comrade has found with deep realization that he has no home, no brother—even no mothers or fathers! What must we do here? . . . Yes, the brother, the erstwhile comrade cast out! There is no brother, no family, no deeper mother than the working class. Long live the struggle for true democracy!" (146-47). The vote is taken and it is unanimously decided that Ernst will be cast out; even Tilly, who is at the moment carry-ing Ernst's child, finally votes to banish Ernst from the party!

After this action, when Ernst is finally released from the Columbia Brown House, he is aware of his almost total per-sonal isolation. He is a shell of a man with no place to turn. Carl doesn't want to hear his explanations, and Ernst says, "You don't want to listen. It's all right—I'll talk to myself. It's a habit now. I talk to myself on the street, frighten children—frighten myself. Don't listen to me. I'll talk to the chair" (150). And so saying, he addresses the chair. Finally, Carl and Tilly realize the desperation with which Ernst speaks and consent to listen to him. By this time Ernst's only concern is that they realize that he has not turned traitor. He says, "I know I must be cast away. But you two can believe me. Yes, officially you need not believe—but yourselves" (152). Even the skeptical Carl is almost convinced, but then he notices that Ernst has a scent of perfume on him and says sarcastically, bitterly: "Perfume? You're using perfume? Lady-fingers and whipped cream for breakfast." And Ernst explains, "They gave me money. It falls out of my hands. My mind wanders like smoke. I passed the store the other day and it was in the window. Perfumed soap. I bought some. A man must have something" (152). He then asks his brother to kill him with a gun which he has brought for the purpose. When Carl cannot bring himself to do this, Ernst goes off to another room and kills himself; but as Carl has said, "They've killed you already" (153).

This play, written rapidly and in a state of great indignation, lacks the verisimilitude of Odets' two earlier plays. The author simply was not sufficiently versed in his material to make *Till the Day I Die* a completely convincing play. Too often he projects his own struggle into it. Despite this, however, the play had an appeal because of the nature of the material treated and was moderately successful during its New York run of ninety-six performances. It went on the road with *Waiting for Lefty* and the twin bill played in thirty-two cities throughout the nation.

The critics varied greatly in their comments on the play. A reviewer for *Time Magazine* felt that "*Till the Day I Die* . . . passes the sixty minute waiting period before *Waiting for Lefty* starts." Brooks Atkinson, writing in the *New York Times,* complained: "If you want to register an emotional protest against Nazi policy, Mr. Odets requires that you join the Communist brethren." On the other hand, Edith Isaacs wrote for *Theatre Arts Monthly* that "*Till the Day I Die* . . . is so far ahead of anything else that Odets has done, in every detail that concerns playwriting, that it escapes comparison with [his other plays]." Most of the critics felt that the play demonstrated skill and that the characterizations were acute and the handling of the scenes competent. In discussing the play in his *Theory and Technique of Playwriting*, John Howard Lawson mentions that he regards Odets as "more of a *scenewright* than a playwright."

Few of the critics recognized some of the developmental tendencies now emerging in Odets' plays. Here, in this play far removed from the Bronx, Odets is laid bare for technical comparison. Of especially great interest is the horrible moment in Scene II when the sadistic Shlegel, having ascertained that Ernst is a violinist and having talked with him about music, brings a rifle butt crashing down on his sensitive hands, thus causing the eventual amputation of Ernst's right hand. The act, horrendous in itself, is made the more terrible when one realizes how much a part of Ernst's life music had been. But the smashing of the violinist's hands has a broader meaning than the horror which is inherent in the very act and which so shocked the audience that Edith Isaacs, writing in *Theatre Arts Monthly*, said that she hoped Odets would ". . . come to know . . . that an audience can feel longer and more deeply the pain in a violinist's mutilated hand if they see the effect of a hammer blow upon it instead of seeing the blow itself."

This act represents the smashing of that which brings comfort—a recurrent theme in Odets' work. As already stated, he wrote a story early in his career about a pianist who had lost his left hand, and later the same theme is to be developed in *Golden Boy* with a special significance; for in this play, Joe Bonaparte, questing after those things which a materialistic society values, sacrifices his hands in order to be a boxer. These instances are basically related, too, to that scene in *Awake and Sing!* in which Bessie Berger storms into Jacob's room in a frenzy and smashes his phonograph records. Her action is motivated by her own insecurity, by her feeling that Jacob's music is something unrealistic intruding into the world of realism which is a necessity to Bessie. But the basic significance of all of these acts seems apparent: some alien force brings about the act which renders enjoyment and fulfillment impossible for the victim. In each of the plays mentioned, the specific act, viewed in this light, reinforces the fundamental theme of the play.

Another theme also begins to emerge in this play; it has to do with the problem which young people face in a time of economic or social upheaval of not being able to plan far enough ahead to have a family. In the scene involving the young hack and his girl in *Waiting for Lefty*, the theme is pervasive; in *Awake and Sing!* Uncle Morty's comment about bringing children into the world is a reflection of a very common feeling of the 1930's; and in *Till the Day I Die*, Ernst and Tillie are beset by the same problem when, in Scene I, while the two are observing children in a park, the dialogue runs:

> TILLY: Maybe we could have one like that, a baby I mean.
> ERNST: When the day comes that we don't have to live like rats in sewers.

(112)

This tendency to put off having children is really a step towards extinction, for carried to its ultimate extreme such thinking would result in gradual depopulation.

Till the Day I Die concludes with a note of hope sounded by the principals; however, it does not recommend the immediate action which *Waiting for Lefty* did; nor does it really suggest valid and substantial solutions to the problems with which it deals. The play lacks clear outlines and consistent point of view, except in the most general sense of its showing sympathy with the poor and oppressed. Stark Young, who reviewed the play for *New Republic*, was quite correct in his suggestion that in this play Odets ". . . needs to establish the plane, indicate the measure, of his various motivations. Taking any of his situations, there is still room for a more important interpretation."

IV *Paradise Lost*

As has been mentioned in Chapter I, *Paradise Lost* was a pivotal play in the career of Clifford Odets. The play suffered from much unjust and shallow criticism, often from generally reliable critics. Joseph Wood Krutch, for example, writing in *The Nation*, said that *Paradise Lost* ". . . seems like nothing so much as an improbable burlesque of *Awake and Sing!*. Apparently the idea was that if a play about a somewhat neurotic family in the Bronx was good, then a play about a madhouse similarly located would be very much better." Krutch felt that "Mr. Odets has lost his reason from too much brooding over the Marxian eschatology."

Paradise Lost is easily comparable in theme and development to *Awake and Sing!;* however, the Gordon family is not characterized as being particularly Jewish, nor is it at the same basic level of society as the Berger family is. The Bergers are of the working class, striving towards the middle class; the Gordons, distinctly of the middle class from the outset, are caught in the dilemma facing this segment of society at a time when it is collapsing economically. Its members, Anita Block pointed out in *The Changing World in Plays and Theatre*, cannot understand ". . . their inability and, even worse, the inability of their children, to whom they have given an education, any longer to 'succeed' in the business and professional world." This class of people—basically conservative, resisting change because of the insecurities which have accompanied changes in their lifetimes—senses something very wrong about society; but it is not sure what this "something" is. The middle-class individual, according to Harold Clurman's introduction to the play, has only the ". . . bewildering perception that everything he intimately believes is being denied by the actual conditions of contemporary society." Clurman goes on to explain that this decay in the middle class during the Depression era was manifested in two facts:

> The two most striking facts of the middle-class situation today are: first, the economic insecurity that deprives it of its former prestige as the bulwark of civilization, and inspires it with a fear of becoming reduced to a social class which it has always considered itself superior to; second, an awareness has grown upon the middle class that most of the ideas by which it has lived no longer correspond to the reality around it.

(12)

It is clear that middle-class standards during this period were outmoded and often downright false. It was these false values which Odets was attempting to expose to objective analysis. His techniques in doing so were basically and generally misunderstood, for many of the reviews ran parallel to that of Gilbert Gabriel, which stated: ". . . everything that would reduce the fiery attractiveness of an *Awake and Sing!* to fog, almost to foolishness, has turned up in exaggerated quantity in *Paradise Lost* and made of it a grotesque with a dozen oratorical arms and not a leg to stand on." This overall opinion was echoed by Richard Lockridge who, writing in the *New York Sun*, called the play a mixture of shrill melodrama and caricature and felt that Odets' faith in the revolution was leading him into unreality. Lockridge said that the play, were it less realistic, might lead the reader to ". . . suspect the author of symbolism."

And here, of course, he stated the basic cause of the misunderstanding of the play. Obviously, neither Odets nor any other practiced playwright would fail to acknowledge the incredibility of having so much misfortune befall a single family in the course of three years as befell the Gordons: Leo, the father, loses his business, bilked by his partner; one son, Julie, is dying from encephalitis; the other son Ben, a former Olympic runner, marries, is unable to support his wife and family, finally resorts to robbery, and is killed by the police; the daughter Pearl, an accomplished pianist, finding that there is no place for art in the world about her, sends her fiancé away and virtually withdraws from the world; the family is evicted after Leo's business goes into bankruptcy. This concentration of disaster is unconvincing unless one remembers that Odets himself, in a *New York Times* interview, said that "clearly . . . my interest was not in the presentation of an individual's problems, but in those of a whole class. . . . The task was to find a theatrical form with which to express the mass as hero." While Odets said this of *Awake and Sing!*, it is equally applicable to *Paradise Lost*.

Despite the realism with which *Paradise Lost* is presented, the play is meant to be taken symbolically, and is convincing only if the symbolic meaning is considered. Anita Block stresses the need for the audience to make a mental effort ". . . to meet the earnest, challenging effort of the dramatist," and she promises that *Paradise Lost* will richly reward those who make such an effort. The play does much more than point to those evils of capitalism which destroy yet another family of the middle class. Odets is not for a moment trying to imply that only *a* family is destroyed; indeed, a huge segment of society is being swallowed up—morally, economically, spiritually—in one of the most pervasive social upheavals to occur in the United States during its history. The author is concerned in *Paradise Lost* with this all-encompassing social situation which he portrays microcosmically through one very limited group of characters. It is through these characters and a knowledge of what each represents that one comes to the fuller meaning of the play which caused Odets to herald this as his ". . . best and most mature play." In it the author attempts to come to grips with every social problem which confronted the middle class in the mid-1930's.

Leo Gordon sets the scene aptly when, early in the first act, he muses that "The world has a profound dislocation." Leo is representative of the honest, conscientious, trusting, middle-class liberal. He is a dreamer who permits Sam Katz, his partner in a firm that manufactures handbags, to run the financial affairs of the business until he becomes aware of the fact that in the shop "the girls work for one dollar a day—nine hours. Forty-five hour week. Five dollars for girls a week, seven dollars for men. But on pay day Mr. Katz makes us sign statements we get more—thirteen and seventeen. Is this fair, gentlemen? On the wall it reads in the labor code, 'Only eight hours' day.' Where is it fair?" (185). Now Leo, the idealist, insists that these conditions be remedied, despite Sam's pleadings that to assume any additional expense at this time will put them into bankruptcy. Leo, caught in a dilemma, will not compromise with his ideals and insists that the employees be dealt with fairly. The result is that in time the business fails; that the Gordons lose the house in which they have lived for seventeen years; that the social forces which, for Odets, typify the 1930's, close in on this now obsolete member of society, the small businessman. Leo's last speech is really a beginning rather than an ending, however, because the speaker still retains his ideals and looks to a future which offers hope. His speech, lengthy though it is, bears quoting in full; it is, in a sense, the essence of the play.

There is more to life than this! . . . We dare to understand. Truly, truly, the past was a dream. But this is real! To know from this that something must be done. That is real. We searched; we were confused! But we searched, and now the search is ended. For the truth has found us. For the first time in our lives—for the first time our house has a real foundation. Clara, those people outside are afraid. Those people at the block party whisper and point. They're afraid. Let them look in. Clara, my darling, *listen to me.* Everywhere now men are rising from their sleep. Men, men are understanding the bitter black total of their lives. Their whispers are growing to shouts! They become an ocean of understanding! *No man fights alone.* Oh, if you could only see with me the greatness of men. I tremble like a bride to see the time when they'll use it. My darling, we must have only one regret—that life is so short! That we must die so soon. . . . Yes, I want to see that new world. I want to kiss all those future men and women. What is this talk of bankrupts, hatred . . . they won't know what that means. Oh, yes, I tell you the whole world is for men to possess. Heartbreak and terror are not the heritage of mankind! The world is beautiful.

[74]

No fruit tree wears a lock and key. Men will sing at their work, men will love. Ohhh, darling, the world is in its morning . . . and *no man fights alone!* . . . Let us have air . . . Open the windows.

(229-30)

One might almost conclude that Leo was living his life according to the code set forth by Jacob in *Awake and Sing!*, for the foundation of his entire existence is love, and his love begets love. If Jacob could say ". . . in a society like this today people don't love," Leo could offer proof of the opposite. Granted, society pressed Leo into a situation which made his love all the more unique; but there he stood, the symbol of how man can survive the most crushing defeats. Sam Katz, the practical businessman, had, in the last analysis, less actual stamina than did Leo, thus indicating that the life which is based upon love and trust is the life which will endure. Leo can always face society squarely because he has not violated its codes, nor has he permitted himself to be victimized by them. His furniture may be out in the street, but a man with the hope which he displays is a silent conqueror. He can sincerely and with profound insight say, "Maybe each hour is for some profound purpose . . . we want to hug the world in our arms" (190).

Sam Katz, the unscrupulous businessman, is also representative of something larger than a single individual. Sam, desirous of having progeny, remains childless and blames the situation on his long-suffering wife, one of the less convincing characters in the play. He taunts her, occasionally beats her, complains publicly of her barrenness, and thoroughly humiliates her. But in a crucial moment the fact is revealed that it is Sam himself who is responsible for not having offspring. He is impotent. His impotence has brought about his downfall, has led to his pilfering funds from the business. This impotence is a highly charged symbol of the inability of the middle-class industrialist to create a future because of the economic situation about him. So Sam, who cannot create a future, wants at least to destroy the present; and this desire is true on both levels of interpretation, the literal and the symbolic. He does all in his power to destroy his marriage by dealing with his wife in an inhuman way; he seeks also to destroy his factory by bringing in May, the professional arsonist, to obliterate the symbol and remembrance of his personal failure.

Katz's wife Bertha and Gordon's wife Clara are not really very dissimilar. Both are typical middle-class women who accept their lots cheerfully and who fully expect life to go on as it always has. They have a reasonable feeling of material security. Both are in sharp contrast to Bessie Berger, who lacked the material security which would have represented a stabilizing influence in the Berger family. The basic difference between Clara and Bertha is that Clara has a happy marriage and has found fulfillment in her three children but that Bertha, because of her childlessness, has been the subject of her husband's abuse and the taunts of her acquaintances. Her great hurt is revealed several times throughout the play, as when she says longingly, "If I had a boy I would buy gold toys" (197). Her relationship to Katz is almost that of protectress. She understands him as fully as anyone is ever likely to; but despite this fact he abuses her continually and she, the victim of his insecurity, loves him in her own way. Her closing remarks towards the end of Act II after Sam's embezzlement has been revealed, are very telling and poignant in their simplicity: "He's a good boy—(Goes up to SAM. Helps him up from lower step. Wipes his face with handkerchief.) We'll go home, Sam" (215).

The basis for Clara's love of Leo is somewhat different, for although on the surface Leo seems more dependent that Sam, he actually is not. He is fortified by an inner strength, as his final speech reveals. Clara and Leo love and respect each other and themselves. Katz, lacking self-respect, destroys all semblance of respect which he might have for his wife by degrading her utterly. Her love is based upon pity because there is nothing about Katz which she can honestly respect.

The Gordon's three children comprise an impressive symbolic element in the play. Pearl, the only girl, is a gifted pianist who is in love with Felix, a fine violinist. They cannot afford to be married because Felix cannot find employment as a musician. Pearl, representing the artist caught in the economic plight of the early days of the Depression, can find no place for herself in society, hence she withdraws from it as completely as she can. She has hardened herself to disappointment, insulated herself against regret; hence, when Felix announces that he must leave to find work elsewhere, Pearl is incapable of protesting, but can only say to the nonplused Felix: "Don't smoke in bed . . . Don't be sentimental" (183). These words actually represent a rather damning indictment of the sort of economic system which forces one to ignore human emotions and simply live to avoid any emotional pain. Pearl has virtually ceased to be a person; she is a cardboard figure because she has come to maturity in the midst of a turbulent socio-economic situation. Even when, in the very end of the play, her piano must be taken away, there is no indication that Pearl feels anything, not even dull pain at its loss.

The older of the Gordon sons, Ben, has never entirely grown up and has, basically, rather primitive emotions. A former Olympic champion, Ben is now unable to run because of a weak heart. He has promises of help from many sources—a berth on Wall Street is the one most often mentioned. But his only tangible help comes from his family which gives him small day-to-day handouts. Even on his marriage night he has to ask his mother for money to take his bride to the movies. After his marriage, the handouts come from his friend Kewpie, through his wife. Ben does not know enough about human motivation to realize that Kewpie is usurping his position as head of the household and as husband.

The great headline hero of former days, Ben is now the hero only in a most circumscribed area. Even his wife does not respect him. Ben is not able to cope with life once the falseness of the standards by which he has always lived become clear to him. Thus, when Kewpie, much to Ben's joy, finds work for him, Ben, though he knows the work is dishonest, plunges right into it in a last desperate attempt to gain the one thing which society respects: money. But Ben has lost all will to live, for he now knows fully the mendacity of middle-class existence. Hence, when he was caught committing a robbery, "He stood there soaking up cop's bullets like a sponge——A guy with fifty medals for running. Ben Gordon wanted to die!" (223). And so saying, Kewpie can exonerate himself of all responsibility for Ben's death—provided he does not ask the question, "Why did Ben Gordon want to die?"

Julie, the other son, works in a bank as the play opens, and is, in a purely theoretical sense, a business tycoon. His is a world of utter unreality. His dream is always *if* ". . . I had a real initial thousand! I'd be fifty-two thousand to the good!" (165). But Julie's life, which is fast running its course because he is incurably ill with encephalitis, represents ". . . an apparently normal capitalism that is dying without knowing it," according to Harold Clurman. As his illness progresses, Julie, who remains with the middle-class family, witnesses its ruin and downfall before he finally dies. So also, in the eyes of Odets, will a sickly capitalistic system remain with the middle class until it is ruined.

Gus Michaels, whose daughter Libby marries Ben, has been a lifelong friend of the Gordon family. Gus was a small businessman, but his business failed and now he does little of anything except collect stamps. He lives with the Gordons. The paradise which is lost in the play is essentially that for which Gus has a deep nostalgia. He is ". . . forever hungerin' for the past. It's like a disease in me, eatin' away . . . some nights I have cried myself to sleep—for old Asbury Park days; the shore dinners at old Sheepshead Bay. . . . In those days every house had its own dog" (207). Of course, Odets is implying here that the overconcern with the visceral aspects of human existence is a part of the weakness of the middle class. The strength of Leo Gordon, in comparison, is in the fact that his standard for measuring the worth of human existence is more spiritual than is that of the average member of middle-class society. Gus represents a sort of solidarity in the ranks of the middle class, however. He benefits from this solidarity by receiving significant and continued aid from Leo; however, when Leo needs help, Gus sacrifices the only thing which is left to him, his stamp collection, and turns the proceeds from it over to the Gordons.

Kewpie symbolizes very vitally the social changes which occurred between the 1920's and the 1930's. In the 1920's the Gordons were prosperous and highly respectable. Kewpie, a petty gangster, would not have been admissible into their society. But with the cataclysmic economic and cultural readjustment of the 1930's, Kewpie's social stature has altered to the point that he can be on intimate terms with a family such as the Gordons. In broader terms, the questionable elements of society begin to make inroads on the conservative, respectable middle class. Ultimately this undesirable force is responsible for the death of, as well as the disillusionment of, the figure who represents the ultimate attainment of middle-class youth, the Olympic champion Ben. The reason is obvious: money talks, and Kewpie, like the bootleggers and confidence men of the period, has money. Presumably his entire life has been spent in growing into what he now is. But when Ben, brought up in an atmosphere of middle-class respectability, tries to follow the shifting economic and social tide, when he capitulates to the temptation of seeking ill-gotten gains, he proves himself incapable and his existence ceases.

Finally, Mr. Pike, the ex-itinerant worker, now a furnace man, represents America's pioneer stock; but he has developed an acute understanding of the economic dilemma of his times and of the problems facing the working class. His utterances are generally philosophical and he is in agreement with the Marxian socio-economic ideal as the solution to the ills of the world and of a struggling mankind. He is, admittedly, working towards an ideal which cannot be fully accomplished, but his philosophy in this regard is quite well summed up when he says, ". . . so in the end nothing is real. Nothing is left but our memory of life. Not as it is . . . as it *might* have been" (224).

The characters in the play are interestingly juxtaposed. Sam and Leo are similar to Kewpie and Mr. Pike, respectively, in every essential respect except that of position on the social scale. It is also interesting to note that Odets implies that each level of society reacts distinctly to specific types of character. Moe Axelrod and Kewpie are very much alike; however, Moe blends into the Berger family which is essentially working class; the Bergers feel a sort of kinship to him. But Kewpie, despite the social changes of the 1930's, cannot be assimilated into the middle-class Gordon family. On the other hand, in *Awake and Sing!* Jacob and Ralph are the butts of cruel jokes; they are thoroughly misunderstood, while Leo and Mr. Pike in *Paradise Lost* are respected and honored because the middle class is more in harmony with the idealist than is the working class. In *Awake and Sing!*, Hennie is presented in the light of her own problems, while in *Paradise Lost*, Libby, the character who corresponds to Hennie, is seen in the light of the problems which she creates.

Odets, in a statement to the press, offhandedly called his play Chekhovian and the result was that some critics assumed that Odets had been enormously influenced by Chekhov. Actually, it is doubtful that Odets had read any Chekhov until some time after *Paradise Lost* had been produced.[13] He had referred to the Russian author only as a point of historic reference and, as Clurman has pointed out in the preface to this play, Odets is actually more exactly comparable to Sean O'Casey than to Chekhov. Of the oft-mentioned literary relationship between Odets and Chekhov, N. B. Fagin writes in the *Texas Quarterly* that *The Cherry Orchard* ". . . lends itself . . . to universal historical analogy. And it was in this sense that Clifford Odets offered his Chekhovian *Paradise Lost* to the American theatre in 1935." However, it is only in this very broad sense that the play may be looked upon as Chekhovian.

V Golden Boy

When Odets left New York for Hollywood after it had become evident that *Paradise Lost* was destined to be a commercial failure, many critics and people in the theatre assumed that this would mark the end of what had been a singularly promising Broadway career. However, these prophets were not correct, for in 1937 Odets returned to New York with the manuscript of what was to be the greatest commercial success of his career, *Golden Boy*. On the surface this play marked a departure from the author's previous works in that it was not quite so obvious in its political pronouncements as the earlier plays had been, nor was the story one of creeping economic paralysis such as that dramatized in *Waiting for Lefty*, in *Awake and Sing!*, and in *Paradise Lost*. The effect of the author's Hollywood experience shows itself in the pat plot and characterization of the play. The characters are sharply drawn, for the most part, and are presented in their most essential aspects with telegraphic brevity.

The story is basically one of rather obvious allegorical significance. Joe Bonaparte, the son of an Italian fruit vendor, has become an accomplished violinist. But in the competitive capitalistic system, he realizes that ". . . down in the street . . . it's war! Music can't help me there" (264). He therefore develops his pugilistic ability, which will help him "down in the street" and give him the one thing which matters in the competitive society which he knows: economic superiority. He gains this popular form of success by rising to the top of the world of boxing, but in so doing he injures his hands so that he can never again play the violin. Ultimately Joe unintentionally kills the former champion by dealing him a blow containing ". . . the fury of a lifetime" (312). In so doing, he sees that he has murdered himself and that he cannot go on with his fighting career. But now he cannot turn to his musical career either; his hands are those of a boxer, not those of a violinist. The play ends with Joe's death in an automobile collision.

Harold Clurman has suggested that *Golden Boy* is Odets' most subjective play and that it was meant to represent the compromise that Odets made with commercialism when he went to Hollywood. Up to the time at which this play was written this analogy is acceptable; but the output of Odets' later years would not indicate that the compromise he made was nearly so complete or final as that which Joe Bonaparte made. But, regardless of this, it is apparent that the play is ultimately concerned with the conflicting forces in life which draw men simultaneously in opposite directions. The violin and the boxing gloves represent antitheses which the play indicates are irreconcilable. It is obvious which of these polar symbols represents the constructive force, which the destructive; it is equally obvious throughout the play which of these forces most often dominates human existence. Joe realizes the pointlessness of what he is doing: "I develop the ability to knock down anyone my weight. But what point have I made? . . . I went off to the wars 'cause someone called me a name— because I wanted to be two other guys. Now it's happening . . . I'm not sure I like it" (282). But now there is no way out for Joe; he is caught in a whirlpool called "success" by what Odets considers a sick society. And in this whirlpool he is pulled irresistibly towards the center with a dizzying speed which can end only in his death.

Odets generally handles the characters in *Golden Boy* with

respect and understanding. In an interview after the opening of the play, the author stated that he was trying to place his hero ". . . in his true social background and show his fellow-conspirators in their true light, [to] bring out the essential loneliness and bewilderment of the average citizen, not [to] blow trumpets for all that is corrupt and wicked around the little Italian boy, not [to] substitute a string of gags for reality of experience, [but to] present the genuine pain, meaning and dignity of life within [the] characters."

Odets' respect for the dignity of life is felt in every character in this play with the possible exception of Eddie Fuseli, the racketeer. Lorna Moon may call herself a tramp from Newark, but she shows gratitude, deep love, understanding. Tom Moody may seem to exploit Joe unmercifully, as when he says, "Joe does his work, I do mine. Like this telephone—I pay the bill and I use it" (288). But what forces Moody into this exploitation of Joe is made clear earlier in the play when he says to Lorna of Joe's fighting career, "It's our last chance for a decent life . . . we have to make that kid fight! He's *more* than a meal ticket—he's everything we want and need from life!" (261). Tokio, Joe's trainer, is a wholly sympathetic character; and so are such minor characters as Barker, the Chocolate Drop's trainer, who stands weeping when the Chocolate Drop is felled by Joe's fatal blow.

The family in *Golden Boy* is very effectively portrayed. Rather than being in the forefront of the action as it was in *Awake and Sing!* and in *Paradise Lost*, it becomes a potent force in the background of the action in *Golden Boy*. In this background are the representatives of the real values in life as portrayed by Mr. Bonaparte and his philosophizing crony, Mr. Carp; or by Anna and Siggie, who are striving to build upon love while Joe is building his career upon hatred; or by Joe's brother Frank, who, as a conscientious representative of the Congress of Industrial Organizations, can say, "I fight [for] . . . the pleasure of acting as [I] think! The satisfaction of staying where [I] belong, being what [I am] . . . at harmony with millions of others" (318). Odets clearly demonstrates here that he is not opposed to fighting for objectives which he considers worth-while, for socially desirable ends; but what Joe is fighting for is not such an end. Early in the play, in a bit of dialogue between Mr. Bonaparte and Mr. Carp, Odets reveals the falseness of the sort of activity in which Joe is engaging:

> CARP: (looking at newspaper) Look! Four or five pages—baseball—tennisball—it gives you an idea what a civilization! You ever seen a baseball game?
> MR. BONAPARTE: No.
> CARP: Hit a ball, catch a ball . . . believe me, my friend —nonsense!
>
> (250)

The credibility of Odets' story in *Golden Boy* has been questioned by a number of critics. The question most frequently raised is whether it is believable that a man with the sensitive hands of a violinist could, in reality, become a successful boxer. In this regard, Professor Gassner has mentioned that many convincing plays begin with spurious hypotheses, but that these do not destroy convictions so much at the beginning of a play as they would if they appeared later in the drama. However, in view of the allegorical significance of *Golden Boy*, the question of credibility assumes less importance than it would if the entire play were intended as a literal representation. It is quite clear that Odets chose the prize-fighting business to represent the world of competition in general, as Miss Block points out in *The Changing World in Plays and Theatre*, ". . . because it epitomizes the battle for gain shorn of all pretense—at its most brutal and at the same time at its most lucrative and spectacular."

It is of interest to note that, through the action of this play, the only character who undergoes any substantial change of personality is the hero and that in the earlier plays the change during the action was a social one which affected the majority of the characters. Joe's change is dramatic and dynamic. Early in the play the audience is told that Joe thinks that music ". . . is the great cheer-up in the language of all countries" (249). Joe, the sensitive introvert, has found his only solace and assurance in music: "With music I'm never alone when I'm alone.—Playing music . . . that's like saying, 'I am man. I belong here. How do you do, World—good evening!' When I play music nothing is closed to me. I'm not like the streets" (262). Joe bares much of his psychological conflict in this speech, for in reality he is a frightened little boy trying to establish his status in a world which might be unwilling to receive him on what he considers adequate terms. "Here Odets shows us a psychological conflict within the individual as devastating as anything O'Neill has portrayed," writes Anita Block; "but he relates it clearly to its social causes, to the false standards of life thrust on the individual by a competitive society."

One of the symbols of the false standards to which Joe is falling victim is his new Deusenberg automobile. This is a very significant symbol because it represents not only the type of materialistic goal which is driving Joe on so forcefully, but also speed, which becomes an important aspect of the play. Speed has become a pervasive factor in modern American existence, since it is integrally a factor in any competitive system. Joe addresses this point when he says, "Those cars are poison in my blood. When you sit in a car and speed you're looking down at the world. Speed, speed, everything is speed—nobody gets me!" (266). That this automobile, a symbol of Joe's success, is also to be a means of death is evident at the beginning of the play when Moody says that he had managed heavyweight contender "Cy Webster who got himself killed in a big, red Stutz" (238). Allusions to Joe's wild driving continue to occur throughout the play, making it increasingly evident that the new Deusenberg is a dangerous instrument in his hands. But this is Joe's nature: Speed has been a force which has shaped his entire life. Rapid success has been a necessity for him, and it has forced him into boxing in the first place.

Not all of the symbolism in *Golden Boy* has lent itself to clear interpretation. In *American Playwrights,* Miss Flexner writes: "There is some unclear symbolism, such as the significance of Fuseli and his relationship to Joe, and the latter's own optical affliction (he is crosseyed and a good deal is made of it in the play)." Both of the symbols which Miss Flexner has mentioned seem quite important. Fuseli is the Italian racketeer who wants to "buy a piece of Joe" and who tries eventually to squeeze out the other shareholders and to manage Joe himself. It is important to remember that Fuseli is Italian, as is the Bonaparte family. He is an immigrant just as Joe's father is. It is obvious, however, that Joe's father represents the philosophically idealistic side of human existence, whereas Fuseli represents the materially oriented and motivated person who gains the commonly recognized symbols of success in a capitalistically oriented society. Joe's father saves for a lifetime in order to buy Joe a twelve-hundred-dollar violin; he goes through life trying to provide his son with a means of self-fulfillment. Fuseli, representing competitive enterprise, buys Joe as though he were a commodity (which to boxing people he is), and he cares nothing about him except as a commodity. Siggie puts it very well when, on meeting Fuseli, he says to his father, "Pop, that's a paradox in human behavior: he shoots you for a nickel—then for fifty bucks he sends you flowers!" (294). Just before the news of Joe's death is received, his brother Frank asks Fuseli, "How much does Joe own of himself?" (319). The question is stingingly provocative.

It is clearly evident that Joe now owns none of himself; he has sold himself completely and there is no turning back. He has left the warm earthy humanity of his home and sold himself in the indifferent world where success is made. The sensitive nestling has reached the age of independence. "Tomorrow's my birthday! I change my life!" (252). And so he changes his life, not to gain independence, but to exchange it for material gain. Even now the break with the past is not complete. His music haunts him. He is knocked out in a fight in Philadelphia because, as Tokio relates, "We run into some man when we're leaving the hotel. Joe goes pale. I ask him what it is. 'Nothing,' he says. But I can see for myself—a man with long hair and a violin case. When we turn the corner, he says, 'He's after me,' he says" (274). The conflict grows in Joe through the next scenes until he finally makes the irrevocable break with music: he breaks his hand and exclaims, "Hallelujah! It's the beginning of the world!" (303). The decision has been made. From this point forth, he always speaks of his love of music in the past tense.

Joe's optical affliction seems representative of his inability to focus on one goal at a time. His emotions are torn and Odets is pointing to ". . . the inevitability of such behavior when human beings are on the one hand pushed to the wall by their circumstances and on the other lack the understanding and the desire to struggle towards a better kind of world."[14] Joe is destined always to look in two directions at once and always to desire what he sees in each direction. The emphasis on Joe's cross-eyed condition is a very useful device to the author. In the first place, on a non-symbolic level, this is one of the factors which made Joe very sensitive in his childhood and which helped to alienate him from his peers. Part of his resentment is attributable to this condition, and his cultivation of music might have its foundation here. When Joe enters the boxing profession, he carries with him his sensitivity about his eyes. But as the play wears on, Joe becomes less and less sensitive about his eyes and, correspondingly, he loses that sensitivity which an artist must have in order to achieve success.

As Joe's sensitivity decreases, he is more and more consumed by resentment of the society which has driven him into boxing, and he finds sublimation for his indignation in the effective use of his fists. He makes the very cogent statement that "people have hurt my feelings for years. I never forgot. You can't get even with people by playing the fiddle. If music shot bullets I'd like it better—artists and people like that are freaks today. The world moves fast and they sit around like forgotten dopes" (264). Joe, out for revenge, directs it against society as a whole. Tokio recognizes this and tells Joe, "Your heart ain't in fighting . . . your *hate* is" (306). Shortly after this statement Joe releases his pent-up fury in a single blow which kills his opponent and, as has been pointed out by Anita Block, Joe "having aligned himself with the destructive forces of society . . . has destroyed—himself."

Golden Boy was received with considerable acclaim, first as a play and later as a motion picture starring William Holden. The play ran for two hundred and forty-eight performances on Broadway, playing to crowded houses throughout the run. The cast was then packed off to London, where the play opened to ovations and had a successful summer run, reopening in the winter with a British cast. Odets sold the movie rights for seventy-five thousand dollars, and the Group Theatre and Odets were sharing unaccustomed prosperity. In this country the road company of *Golden Boy* was playing to large audiences. The San Francisco company was directed by Stella Adler, and the cast included Louis Calhern and Betty Furness. The play had a successful run in Chicago in the autumn of 1938, and it received high praise wherever it was given.

The American National Theatre and Academy presentation of the play was produced in 1952 and represented another critical phase in the history of *Golden Boy*. Louis Kronenberger, writing in *Time Magazine*, felt that "*Golden Boy* . . . though perhaps the most popular Odets play, scarcely ranks among the best." On the same day, T. H. Wenning wrote in *Newsweek* of ". . . a steadily absorbing production of one of Clifford Odets' best plays and his greatest box-office success." Wolcott Gibbs, who had given little favorable comment to most of Odets' plays, pointed out certain weaknesses when he reviewed the play for *The New Yorker,* but he admitted that *Golden Boy* ". . . is an honest and often moving attempt to deal seriously with the war between the need for half-crazy popular success and the instinct for decent, if non-spectacular, accomplishment that is bound to take place in almost any sensitive man in our society today." E. V. Wyatt, writing in *Catholic World,* called the play ". . . a well-knit drama," but she objected to the type of society the author wrote about in the play. Margaret Marshall wrote in the *Nation* that "*Golden Boy* is not a very good play. It is skillfully constructed, but its plot is patently contrived. It has passages that are well conceived and freshly written; it is also ridden with the most ordinary . . . clichés of the socially conscious thirties."

While some critics were crying out that the play was "lacking [in] inner validity, [that] the scenes fail to mesh," others wrote that the play "pulled the dramatic reins tight and shocked its way through the evening like a series of body blows," or that "the dialogue remains as fresh as it was in 1937." The play, since then performed in summer stock and in small theatres throughout the country, seldom fails to attract a substantial audience. The play is continuingly successful, probably because, as John Gassner has mentioned, "in *Golden Boy* Odets was singularly fortunate. Dealing with a piece of Americana for which a common understanding existed, Odets did not have to force too many parallels outside the realistic context of the work. Never again [this was written in 1949] did he light upon another fable that would serve him nearly as well." Despite the great diversity of critical opinion in regard to *Golden Boy*, it seems evident that it represents an historic dramatic event in contemporary American theatre.

VI *The First Five Plays*

One can hardly read the first five plays of Clifford Odets without being keenly aware of the power with which he presents his views of capitalism. At the end of the first major productive period of his career, one can make generalizations about his social outlook. His most obvious concern is, as he has stated himself, with the social mass rather than with the individual. *Golden Boy* may seem to be an exception to this statement; however, if this play is considered on the allegorical rather than the literal level, it becomes evident that Odets is using the individual to represent the mass, just as he used the family in this capacity in *Awake and Sing!* and in *Paradise Lost*. In all of the plays of this early period, the family has emerged as a basic foundation in the social structure; the position of family is obvious in *Awake and Sing!* and in *Paradise Lost*. In *Waiting for Lefty* the consideration of the family as a social force is seen in the episode of the young hack and his girl, in which the forbidding picture of what the present economic chaos might do to a family structure looms in the background, while in the Joe and Edna episode the effect of severe economic hardship upon a marriage relationship is explored. The family is considered, also, in *Till the Day I Die;* but the basic family consideration in this play, as in the Labor Spy episode in *Waiting for Lefty*, is the relationship between two brothers who are separated by distrust. The use of the family in *Golden Boy* has been detailed in the discussion of that play.

Another fundamental social concern in these plays is found in the recurrent implications that economic determination is the most important single force affecting human activity. This concept is basic to each of the plays, and the author's solution to this situation is found in his emphasis on the need for cooperation between people and in his calls for collective action, especially notable in *Waiting for Lefty*, but present also in the early plays as a whole.

The plays ultimately focus on the mendacity of human existence, on the falseness of most human relationships, and on the shallowness of most conventional social values. Odets is calling for the recognition of truth and for the banishment of the false values which dominate the society of which he is writing.

Throughout the plays, Odets writes with a reverence for human beings and with a deep concern for their problems. He is not condemnatory even of the unsympathetic characters in his plays, so much as he is of the social institutions which have forced men to compromise with their ideals in order to survive. Odets constantly calls for the very thing that Jacob wanted in *Awake and Sing!*: dignity in human existence. These early plays are forthright in their criticism and condemnation of anything in life which negates this dignity.

CHAPTER *4*

Love and Marriage

"I don't enjoy my life.
. . . I enjoy only the
dream of it."
(From *Clash by Night*)

IN MANY RESPECTS the short time that Clifford Odets spent
in Hollywood in 1935 and 1937 had a very significant effect
upon him both as a man and as an artist. He had now come
to know not only financial security, but indeed wealth. During this time he was married to Luise Rainer, he had written
the scenario for a moderately successful film, and he was a
center of interest to many of the theatrical personalities both
in New York and in Hollywood. His return to New York with
Golden Boy was triumphal. His company was sought by the
prominent, his pronouncements were printed, his next play
was awaited by an eager following of substantial size.

The earlier Odets plays, notably *Waiting for Lefty, Till the
Day I Die,* and *Awake and Sing!,* had been essentially political and propagandistic in their approach. The author's tendency was essentially leftist, as has been previously mentioned.
This was a drawing-card for many liberals who came to look
upon Odets as a political spokesman first and as a conscious
creative artist only secondarily. This group of liberals was
somewhat disappointed that *Golden Boy,* while filled with
political implications, was not more direct in stating what it
had to say. However, this play was so appealing on a purely
literal level that it won a great deal of favorable comment, as
has been noted in the previous chapter.

Golden Boy represents a transitional period in Odets' writing. It is much broader in scope than the earlier plays, and

shows clearly that the author is unwilling to remain ideologically static and produce political propaganda for the re-
mainder of his life. His concern is for man and the forces
which dictate human destiny—which, in a broader sense, determine the course of the entire human race. Man's relation
to his family is a dominant theme in *Awake and Sing!, Paradise Lost,* and *Golden Boy.* Man's relation to the state is the
basic concern in *Till the Day I Die.* Man's struggle to sustain
himself is an ultimate concern in *Golden Boy,* and, in a less
detailed manner, in all of the early plays. In the period following *Golden Boy,* the emphasis is on a theme which is present
secondarily in all of the earlier plays: the need for life to be
vitalized by love. The three plays in point are *Rocket to the
Moon, Night Music,* and *Clash by Night. Rocket to the Moon*
and *Clash by Night* are primarily concerned with the marriage
relationship; *Night Music* centers upon the problem of young
love. The increased interest in the question of marriage was
motivated by the fact that Odets himself was married in 1937.
His marriage to Miss Rainer very nearly ended the following
year, but the divorce action of 1938 was withdrawn. The
marriage was terminated by divorce in 1941.

To the audience awaiting the appearance of a second
Waiting for Lefty, the Odets of the late 1930's and early 1940's
presented a great disappointment. The anger of the young
rebel had cooled somewhat with the passage of the years and
with the amelioration of some of the conditions which had
earlier aroused his ire. But Odets had not ceased to feel social
concern; he was, as John Gassner indicated in writing about
Rocket to the Moon in the *One Act Play Magazine,* ". . . still
wrestling with society, still trying to break its stranglehold on
life. His attack is merely different . . . He has always been at
heart a 'synthesist' who tries to combine individual experiences
into a social whole . . . Odets has always tended to see social
forces concretized in human beings." This statement may be
applied generally to the three plays which comprise this mid-
dle-span in Odets' creative life. All of the plays are concerned
with problems which are connected with economic insecurities and pressures.

The plays of the period from 1938-42, as will be seen, do not
have the verve of Odets' earlier plays. Still, they contain some

memorable moments: the continued use of fresh, crisp dialogue is notable; and, even though the author is writing about the rather drab existence of extremely banal people, the action does not settle down into the sort of dreary bathos which would have been inevitable had the subjects been treated by a less versatile and sensitive author.

I *Rocket to the Moon*

Rocket to the Moon, produced by the Group Theatre in November, 1938, was originally intended to be a vehicle for Odets' new wife, Luise Rainer. However, the uncertainty of the relationship between the author and his wife during the first year of their marriage resulted in the appointment of Eleanor Lynn as the female lead in a version of the play considerably altered from Odets' original outline. Odets had originally intended that the play's hero, Ben Stark, be portrayed as a meek, insignificant dentist who is ravaged with love for his receptionist, a young woman of questionable mentality but of distinct physical attractiveness. Through this love, Ben was to have grown and matured beyond his normal expectations, and would, as a result, have emerged as the central character in the play. As the play finally developed, the central figure is the childish little romantic, Cleo; and the theme, rather than being one of growth through love, is one depicting the extreme difficulty of finding love or anything even approximating it in modern society.

The theme of barrenness, which had been considered in earlier Odets plays, permeates the action of *Rocket to the Moon* rather fully. Ben's wife Belle has lost their child during childbirth, and she can have no more children. Her longing for a child, suggestive of the longing of the Katzes in *Paradise Lost,* manifests itself in constant complaining, nagging, and suspicion. Ben's only retreat from this unfortunate situation is into his office, which he shares with a fellow dentist, Phil Cooper. Phil is so drawn by Odets as to represent the plight of the professional man caught in the throes of the Depression. His future is much less secure that that of Ben Stark, who earns a fairly steady sixty dollars a week. Phil has so few patients that he is not able to pay his share of the rent; disheartened by his situation, he drinks rather steadily throughout the course of the play.

Belle's father, Mr. Prince, is a finely delineated character. His marriage has been unhappy; now that his wife is dead, his daughter is very unfriendly and, at times, even hostile toward him. Mr. Prince is a successful businessman, a shrewd speculator in the stock market, who has ". . . offered to put [Ben] in a swell office." But Ben "likes it here."* Mr. Prince would like to be a lover, but at his advanced age he cannot be and he becomes more and more a victim of boredom. He is searching for the warmth and love which have been denied him throughout his life by both his wife and his daughter.

Mr. Wax, a choreographer and director, and Frenchy, a chiropodist whose office is near Ben's, complete the cast of characters aside from Cleo, the receptionist, around whom much of the play revolves. Cleo, who is trying to make a living in the difficult days of the Depression, has had a difficult time because of her rather limited background and ability. She lives on dreams because the realities about her are too disheartening to face.

The play opens with tension between Ben and his wife. She does not want to see him open the office which her father has offered him. She is also agitated because he has given his receptionist an increase in salary and because Phil Cooper has not been able to pay his share of the rent for some months. She is attempting, somewhat highhandedly, to protect Ben from all the people who might take advantage of him. This is obviously a prototypical action in a woman who direly needs the responsibility of rearing a child but, lacking this opportunity, finds an outlet for her mother instincts in being overly protective of her husband, who neither needs nor desires her protection and who finds it a continual source of embarrassment to him.

Odets increases the tension of the first act very convincingly. To begin with, the act is taking place on a hot day in June when nerves would tend to be somewhat strained. As soon as the basic tension between husband and wife has been estab-

Six Plays of Clifford Odets, p. 368. All page citations for *Rocket to the Moon* will refer to this edition of the play.

lished, Cleo the receptionist enters the scene. Belle, in a testy manner, picks at Cleo:

> BELLE: You're dressed to kill, Miss Singer.
> CLEO: That's one of my ordinary everyday dresses—angel-skin satin.
> BELLE: It looks hot.
> CLEO: It's one of my coolest dresses.
> BELLE: Is that why you don't wear stockings?
> CLEO: Yes.
> BELLE: I thought maybe to save money.
> CLEO: I come from a well-to-do family.
> BELLE: How well-to-do?
> CLEO: I don't need this job.
> BELLE: (archly) Nevertheless, as long as you have the job, you should wear stockings in the office.

(336)

This sort of unpleasantness is not just a passing mood with Belle; it has become a normal pattern of behavior, inherited, one is led to believe, from her mother, and now reinforced by her own barrenness. Belle is very useful in providing a detailed sketch of her husband as a meek, spineless man crushed as a person, seeking, but not expecting to find, a true purpose in life. Belle's venom is next directed against Phil Cooper, who is already crushed by his poverty and by the knowledge that he has a very bleak future ahead of him. But Belle knows no pity; her own insecurity and frustration cause her to be hard and embittered, unmitigatingly cruel to those who display any form of personal weakness. Belle feeds on weakness in others and uses such flaws to mask her own inadequacies.

Cleo, a young woman who is also very insecure, is, on the other hand, essentially sympathetic, willing to give of herself and gracious in receiving what others have to offer her. Naïve, she finds herself deceived at times, but she does not let such deceptions make her bitter; rather she accepts them as part of her experience and puts them from her mind as quickly as she can. At this juncture in her life, Cleo needs passion, security, glamor. Since she cannot find these three qualities in any one man of her acquaintance, she, like Nora Leeds in O'Neill's *Strange Interlude,* encourages the attentions of three

men, each representing to her one of the requisite necessities
of her life. Odets might have commented on which of these
three qualities is most important; but Cleo does not make a
choice among the three men—Ben, Mr. Prince, and Mr. Wax.
Instead she departs to find her own way, having said:

> I'm a girl, and I want to be a woman, and the man I love must
> help me be a woman! Ben isn't free. He's a citizen of another
> country. And you, Mr. Prince, don't let me hurt your feelings:
> you've lived your life. I think you're good, but you're too old
> for me. And Mr. Wax, his type loves himself. None of you can
> give me what I'm looking for: a whole full world, with all the
> trimmings.
>
> (416-17)

One might say that in view of her attributes, Cleo expects considerably more than she is ever likely to find, but her attitude
is consistent with the overall theme of the play. Cleo leaves
things substantially as they were when the play began. Possibly Belle has grown somewhat through the knowledge of her
husband's interest in Cleo; she at least promises to forgive him
for it and to try to start their life together over again. Ben is
hopeful of the future as he sits down in his office after Cleo's
departure and says, "For years I sat here, taking things for
granted, my wife, everything. Then just for an hour my life
was in a spotlight. . . . I saw myself clearly, realized who and
what I was. Isn't that a beginning?" (418). Unfortunately,
the hope which Ben feels cannot be shared by an acute audience. Belle is so convincing as the harridan that it is not easy
to imagine that she will undergo any change sufficient to make
her lovable. Also, the fact that her mother was so unsympathetic to Mr. Prince makes one wonder whether Belle, brought
up in such an atmosphere, has ever known any feeling but
resentment towards the entire male sex.

Mr. Prince represents the philosophical element in *Rocket to
the Moon*. He is kindly and understanding, genuinely fond of
his son-in-law, and pathetic in his loneliness. It is interesting to
note that Mr. Prince is the only figure in the play who has any
real financial security; yet it does him little good because he
cannot find in life the one vitalizing element that his whole
being calls out for—love. He is dissatisfied with himself and

with the course which his life has followed. He expresses this feeling when he says, "Yes, Benny, I started from an idealist, too, believe it or not. Now I'm a villain" (346). He continues, "Where is she hiding, happiness?" Mr. Prince's marriage has prevented him from fulfilling his deepest desires in life. "Without marriage I would have been one of the greatest actors in the world! . . . All my life I wanted to do something" (347).

This situation is obviously the same as the one in which Ben finds himself. He, too, wants to do something. Despite Belle's comment that "Ben likes it here [in his office]," Ben wants something more. He would like to accept the offer of his father-in-law and open a large office in a more fashionable neighborhood, but Belle will not let him. Similarly, Belle blocks every chance that Ben has for fulfillment; she is the stumbling block in his romance with Cleo. It is because of her barrenness that she and Ben have no children. It is difficult to believe that these factors will change or can be ignored to the extent that they will ever cease to interfere with the Stark marriage. It would seem more likely that Odets is implying that it is very difficult to find love and that most love is based, at best, upon the sort of compromise involved in Ben's returning to Belle.

Phil Cooper is typical of many of the Depression figures found in some of Odets' earlier plays. He is beside himself with concern over maintaining himself and his motherless child even on their present hand-to-mouth level. When Belle goads him to pay his share of the office rent, he sums up his problems in a single speech:

> Business won't pick up until after Labor Day. But if the loan company decides to—(*Within the office the telephone rings.* COOPER *quickly opens the door and takes the telephone from* CLEO's *hands.*) Hello? . . . Yes, this is your party . . . yes . . . yes . . . yes . . . (COOPER *hangs up the telephone and trails back into the waiting room* . . .) No, no dice . . . no shoes for baby. . . . I don't know what I'll do with my boy—Children are not like furniture—You can't put them in storage. If his mother was alive . . . (*His speech trails off, and then he says*) When I'm happy I'm a different person. You'd be surprised—everybody likes Phil Cooper.

(338-39)

Phil is sincere and ingenuous. He is one of Ben Stark's most loyal friends, but Belle is relentless in seeing that her husband's accounts are kept balanced regardless of what personal circumstances intervene.

She has the opportunity to compensate for her own childlessness by taking some positive action towards helping Phil's child, but Belle does not appear to possess the altruistic character which would permit her to turn her energies to something constructive. She seems to represent the same sort of impersonal force which, in *Paradise Lost,* forces the Gordon family into the street. She is the antithesis of her father who, in his warmth and consummate humanity, says, "Everything that's healthy is personal" (341). If, as Joseph Wood Krutch states in his *American Drama since 1918,* "Mr. Odets exhibits, among other things, two gifts not often combined—the gift for a kind of literal realism which makes his characters recognizable fragments of reality, and the gift for endowing these same characters with an intensity of life which lifts them into another realm," then surely Belle may be spoken of on more than a single plane. She would appear to have many of the characteristics which Odets has previously imputed to representatives of the capitalistic system, and she would also appear to represent one of the supposed ills of such a system—the ill which, until the beginning of World War II, made it somewhat less than proper for the wives of professional men to work. Had Belle expended her energies in some sort of gainful employment, she would have had little time to torment others and she would probably have had a much happier existence. Belle is more a victim in the play than a villain, for she does not know any more happiness or fulfillment than either her husband or father.

Casting its glow over Ben's office and over his love affair with Cleo is the omnipresent neon sign atop the Hotel Algiers, a nearby establishment of somewhat unsavory reputation. The hotel, which is to recur in *Night Music* as the residence of Fay Tucker, provides a sharp contrast between the type of love which goes on behind its stolid façade and the kind of love which exists between Cleo and Ben; theirs is a love which fills a positive need in both their lives and which has about it a certain purity. It is not the cheap love-for-a-night which the hotel in the background is intended to represent. Mordecai Gorelik's sets for *Rocket to the Moon* tended to emphasize the presence of the hotel and were built ". . . toward an abstract pattern which aims at interpreting the inner meaning of the drama."[1]

On a literal level, the real tragedy of the play is the failure of the love affair between Ben and Cleo. However, if, forgetting for the moment even the moral issues involved, one were to view the situation honestly and in perspective, he would be forced to conclude that a permanent union between these two might hardly be called desirable. Ben has no initiative and does not really want to think for himself. Belle dominates him and those about him only because he permits her to. Bessie Berger dominates her husband in the same way in *Awake and Sing!*, and his only response is "Tell me what to do, Momma." This type of man represents the antithesis of what most women want from a man. In *Clash by Night*, Mae Wilenski, a much more primitive character than either Bessie Berger or Belle Stark, tells what a women expects of a man when she says: "Confidence! He gives you confidence, and he never breaks it down. . . . He gives you consideration, at least as much as he gives the baseball scores. . . . He makes her more of a woman instead of less . . . he beats the world off when it tries to swallow her up." But Ben Stark cannot even take a convincing stand when Cleo goes out with Mr. Prince or Mr. Wax. And it is hardly conceivable that Cleo is, at this point, ready to be a party to any relationship as permanent as marriage. Living in the world of her own illusions, she would be much more likely to rankle under the monotony of marriage than even Belle has.

In *Rocket to the Moon*, then, the deeper tragedy is that which makes complete love, total identity with another person, impossible. Out of this tragedy grows the hulking social problem which is ultimately found in either broken or hopelessly entangled marriages. Odets is convinced, in this play, that man is lonely. He does not postulate love as a permanent solution to this loneliness, but rather implies that it is man's lot that he be lonely. This is the beginning of a theme which reaches fruition in *Clash by Night* and which has been strongly suggested in the characters of Ernst Tausig in *Till the Day I Die*, of Jacob in *Awake and Sing!*, and of Joe Bonaparte in *Golden Boy*.

Rocket to the Moon was never a highly successful play commercially. It ran for one hundred and thirty-one performances on Broadway, and it played this long largely because of the Group Theatre's policy of running numerous benefit performances to which organizations subscribed. Before the play closed, the Group ran it alternately with the revival of *Awake and Sing!*, which drew much larger audiences than *Rocket to the Moon* was able to. The latter play ran for brief engagements in Philadelphia and in Baltimore, but received a cool reception in both cities. A New York revival in 1946 did not prove more successful. The public apparently just did not like the play. Perhaps Odets was writing from too personal a standpoint in it. Perhaps the public would agree with Thornton Wilder, who recently said, "I am not interested in such ephemeral subjects as the adulteries of dentists."[2]

The critics were mixed in their comments about the play. John Gassner probably came closer than most critics to a fair interpretation when he wrote that the ". . . piece stops logically with its demonstration of the failure of love in our society." Joseph Wood Krutch wrote that "*Rocket to the Moon* carried [Odets] at least one step further along the road he is traveling"[3] and praised him for not permitting his Marxian leanings to stand in the way of his artistic development. But Mr. Krutch, it must be remembered, was writing some years after the play was first presented, and he viewed the work in the light of Odets' total development up to the time that the Krutch book was written. Krutch felt that the only political interpretation possible in the play seems ". . . to come down to no more than the suggestion that money or the lack of it plays some part in determining the course which our lives must take."

George Jean Nathan, writing in the *Nation*, felt that Odets had drawn his characters very well, but he complained that the author had nothing new to say. Rosamund Gilder, judging the play more on moral than artistic grounds, wrote in *Newsweek* that she regretted that the play was "concerned less with social justice than with human relationships." Another critic called *Rocket to the Moon* an exercise in dialogue, which to a degree it was, and accused Odets of suffering ". . . from the belief that an epigram is a thought."

Odets did not turn a deaf ear to his critics. Rather, he attempted to strengthen his play in accordance with their suggestions. It had been generally recognized that the play declined from an excellent first act towards a somewhat monotonous ending—towards a "muffed universalism, and a resolution in symbolic banalities," as Stark Young wrote in *New Republic*. The play, considerably longer than the average Broadway production, created practical problems both for the cast and the audiences. In order to overcome some of these problems and to prevent the last two acts from dragging, Odets cut the play considerably; but the response of the audience was no warmer than it had been on opening night. The author refused to follow his wife's suggestion of having Cleo marry Mr. Prince rather than leave Ben's office without having solved any of the basic problems of her life or of the play. Such an ending would have been in character with Cleo as she was presented and would have been a more conclusive ending than the one which Odets insisted upon. Marrying Mr. Prince would have been an obvious out for Cleo.

While the play does represent a broadening in Odets' interests and social concerns, it does not mark an artistic advance for him. It was too much a reflection of his personal problems to be a thoroughgoing work of art.

II *Night Music*

Clifford Odets called *Night Music* "a song cycle on a given theme." The structure of the play is such that it cannot be said to have any strong underlying unity aside from the theme, which is one of homelessness. Willard Thorp has said, in his *American Writing of the Twentieth Century*, that "the substance of an Odets play is the incommunicable loneliness of his characters"; and, as *Night Music* develops, one is increasingly aware of this personal isolation. Among those who have written about the play, few have realized that the seeming aimlessness of the story was not accidental, but actually was quite topical and was calculatedly worked out. Harold Clurman, basing his opinions on extended conversations with the author and on the text of the play, clearly demonstrates that this is the case. In *The Fervent Years,* he reminds one that

> The late winter and early spring of 1940 were as special a period as the days preceding the bank holiday of 1933. There was an unvarying low level of pseudo-prosperity and with it extensive unemployment. The mood in New York might have been characterized as one of intense stagnation. History was marking time. Progressive thought and action seemed to stand in shadow, tired and disheartened. Everyone seemed to be waiting. Everything was in question, and all the old answers rang a little false beside the darkening reality. The tone of the play [*Night Music*] was gentle and melancholy, as if the clarinet the play's hero tooted was his only weapon to combat the featureless chaos of 1940.[4]

If one keeps in mind this social background, the meaning of *Night Music* and the reason for its method becomes somewhat clearer. America was caught in the lull before an inevitable storm, and Odets was keenly aware of how chaotic and menacing the world situation was. He reminds his audiences of this situation by including among the *dramatis personae* of *Night Music* a figure who sits sleeping in the lobby of the Hotel Algiers on a Saturday night because ". . . he's worried. He's got folks in Poland."[*]

Throughout *Night Music,* Odets is writing ". . . in terms of what is not said, of combinations elusive and in detail, perhaps, insignificant, of a hidden stream of sequences, and a resulting air of spontaneity and true pleasure."[5] The character of Julie was developed in this way in *Paradise Lost,* even though the rest of the play was not. But *Night Music* is a play at once subtle and simple, at once direct and evasive. The levels on which it operates are numerous.

The hero of the play, Steve Takis, has been sent East by a Hollywood film studio to accompany two trained apes back to Hollywood, where production on a film is being held up pending their arrival. While he is standing on a Manhattan street corner with the apes and about to go to the airport, they snatch Fay Tucker's locket and the result is that Steve and

---

[*]*Night Music,* Random House Edition, p. 55. Future page citations will be from this edition of the play.

the apes land in the police station. No one can verify Steve's rather peculiar story because it is Saturday and the film company's New York office is not open. Steve, who has lost his wallet in the scuffle of being taken into custody, is released from the precinct station, but his apes are kept as security. Steve looks forward to a very bleak weekend with no money and with the prospect of losing his first real job in some time. Upon his release from jail, he goes to the theatre where Fay is playing a minor role in a play which is, after three performances, about to close. He approaches Fay with a feeling of great indignation; but as the action of Odets' play wears on, the two are drawn to each other and ultimately fall in love.

Steve is young, brash, and boastful. Odets purposely wrote the part so that the audience would dislike him during most of the first act. The young man's brashness is obviously engendered by his insecurity, which is well portrayed. He has, because of his personal and social background, been unable to settle down to any sort of normal existence anywhere and has earned the nickname of Suitcase Steve. His homelessness is one of the first characteristics about him which comes to the attention of the audience.

Fay lacks Steve's brashness, but she does have a mind of her own and a very good idea of what she expects from life. She has left the security of her father's home in Germantown to make a life for herself as an actress in New York. She is living in a hotel which specializes in renting rooms by the hour, but she keeps herself above the tawdry level of existence which surrounds her. She, too, is pictured as being essentially homeless; but she has a more ready and dependable source of material security than Steve has ever known because she can always return to her family if she is unable to look after herself adequately.

Fay has brought about the situation of the play, but has done so unwittingly; she naturally screamed when the apes snatched her locket and this brought the police into the matter. She never intended to cause Steve the difficulties which now confront him. A rather admirable character from the very beginning of the action, she provides a balance for Steve's rather volatile and sometimes irritable disposition.

The third major character in the play is Detective A. L.

Rosenberg of the New York City Police Department. Rosenberg, a benevolent person who loves life, serves as the force which brings Steve and Fay together. Rosenberg understands youth and the social problems which confront it in an age of extreme uncertainty. In his small way he goes about righting that little segment of a disoriented world with which he comes into contact. But Rosenberg, the most significant force for good in the play, is dying of cancer. If the good which he has striven to attain is to have meaning, he must impart some of his admirably optimistic and altruistic spirit to those about him. It is, of course, symbolically significant also that the one positive force for good in the play should be on the brink of death.

Fay's father and Eddie Bellows, her former fiancé, though they appear rather fleetingly in the play, are significant representatives of the forces in society which are opposed to the youthful optimisim of the central characters. They are well-meaning, although Eddie Bellows is somewhat inflated by his own importance; but they cannot face life on such a dynamic and hopeful plane as Steve and Fay can. Steve, when told that a "certain late Cardinal" spoke in the same egalitarian terms which he expresses, shouts out, "He spoke? *Spoke?* Why didn't he do?" (181). This call to action, reminiscent of the closing speech in *Waiting for Lefty,* is a clear indication that what Rosamund Gilder called the ". . . rich, opaque violence that is typical of Odets" is still a potent force in his later writing.

The incidental characters in *Night Music* are ably represented and serve well to strengthen the underlying theme of the play. The man sleeping in the lobby of the Hotel Algiers has already been mentioned. Also in this lobby one meets the sailor who wants a room for himself and a woman, purportedly his wife, who is waiting outside. The sailor is thrown out of the hotel because of the uncertain relationship which exists between the hotel and the vice squad, and he is thereby denied the only pleasure which he can look forward to during his short leave. He, too, is homeless.

Lily, a lady of somewhat questionable virtue, waits in the lobby, expecting a telephone call from an admirer who might ". . . take me to his family's house for supper" (55-56). Lily is a pitiable woman. Alone, she is much in need of the sort of permanence which marriage would offer her. She states her problem rather well as she continues, "I try to be cold, but I can't help it. He gives me a look and I frizzle up." The "he" is almost any "he"—Lily wants only some assurance of love and is not strong enough to discriminate between sincerity and insincerity in what her various admirers say to her. It would take considerable strength of character for a woman of Lily's calibre to admit to herself that what most men say to her is said only because of the expediency of the situation.

Mr. Nichols, who monopolizes the lobby telephone booth, is another example of a person looking desperately for something and not able to find it, principally because he is not entirely sure what he is looking for. He builds his whole life on the sort of expectation that his telephone calls represent.

The desk clerk, Mr. George, was ". . . a well-known figure around New York City" at one time, but has now been forced to submit to the anonymity which is the fate of all hotel clerks.

The most striking example of the homelessness which Odets is concerned with in this play is found in the character of Roy Brown, the young man whom Steve talks with when he goes into the park to spend the night after stalking out of the Hotel Algiers. Roy Brown is first described as a "homeless man" who sits whistling the "Prisoner's Song" to himself. He does not think it is bad to be a prisoner; for, as he says, "As a prime spitter, I had three comfortable days in the jail [when the police arrested people for spitting on the subway]. The first time in weeks I had my three squares a day." Brown has finally decided to join the army because "it settles where I eat and sleep" (86). Odets is here presenting a very dismal view of what man must go through in order to survive. He must, in one way or another, give up his freedom if he is a Roy Brown.

Despite the feeling of despair which the idea of homelessness might suggest, Odets' play is not one which would really suggest pessimism. Joseph Wood Krutch observed in the *Nation* that it is ". . . a sort of romantic extravaganza [emphasizing] the triumph of youthful spirits over the confusions and cruelties of contemporary life." It is noteworthy that Rosenberg should take the two young people to the World's Fair, a place clearly suggesting a bright future. Against this background, Steve does not cease to feel indignation; his resentment is deep and has many sides. He looks about him at the fair and says, "The world of the future! I'd like to meet this Mr. Whiskers. He don't know I'm living, Uncle Sam" (178). Steve's past has not been easy. At times he has had long lapses between jobs. He has been "slammed outa twenty states" and been held for vagrancy in five. However, it was Odets' intention that Steve be represented as thinking that the perplexities which had beset him would not be so great in the future. The strong denunciation speech in the World's Fair scene, while delivered passionately by Elia Kazan in the Group Theatre presentation of *Night Music,* was intended to be spoken wistfully. The speech, outlining the hero's past and pointing toward his future, is worthy of quotation because it is a major pivotal point in *Night Music.*

> You don't know me. I'm a real harmony boy in my heart, if I get a chance. Here *she* is. . . . What kinda life where you gotta compare yourself to crickets? *They're bugs!* You said there'll be a boom? There's a war and there'll be a boom? Sure, boom-boom an' you're dead! Like my father. He's over in France—with a mitt full of poppies. That's why I never got to know him, my own old man. The third gold star in Massachusetts an' don't forget it! . . . I vamp around an' I vamp around an' nothin' happens—you can't get a start. You're keepin' me there on a low A when I'm good enough for a high C! . . . *An' then came the war.* . . . They rub you down with psychology an' brush you off with patriotics! By then you don't care. You're ready to tear some guy to pieces with a bayonet. It gives you pleasure to do it! An' that's what I'm good for . . . an' that's what I'll do . . . that harmony boy who mighta been! . . . Make this America for me. Make this America for her [Fay] and her family—they're shiverin' in their boots. Where is Wilbur Harris: He fell off the freight an' lost a leg. Where's Joe Abrams? Teddy Bannister? In jail. Dan Lowe is pushin' up the daisies—T. B. The sweetest little girl on our block—she's peddling it on the streets! An' where are those other pals of my cradle days? Hangin' up by the ears from coast to coast . . . those harmony boys who mighta been! *Make this America for us!*
>
> (179-80)

In his early twenties, all Steve has ever really known are economic insecurity and the struggle for the barest existence. All he asks is to be able to make his way in life honestly; but even as Odets was writing this play, the unemployed in the United States numbered over ten million. Of course, Steve, speaking bitterly here, was asking for a social revolution. But for any sort of social revolution to succeed and to bring about a positive good, the revolutionaries must show signs of having something positive to offer, something which cannot come to fruition under the prevailing system. There is a large question regarding what positive part Steve could take in making a better world. His general call is "Make this America for us!"; however, he does not seem to have the inner motivation to bring about what he desires.

Night Music represents a departure from other plays by Odets. In *The Theme of Loneliness in Modern American Drama,* Winifred Dusenbury identifies in part what this departure is: "No menacing industrialists are responsible for the boy's despair. The social scheme may have something to do with his situation, but it is only within himself and through contact with a guiding spirit that he can find happiness" (39). In his introduction to the play, Harold Clurman notes that "this play is nearest amongst Odets's plays to our conception of 'pure' entertainment." This, too, is a departure, and Odets' plays after *Night Music* did not approach pure entertainment nearly so closely as this play did.

The action of *Night Music* is condensed into a single weekend, whereas in all of the earlier plays, with the exception of *Waiting for Lefty,* the action covered a more considerable chronological period. The result of the concentration in *Night Music* is not, unfortunately, a heightened intensity, as might be expected. Rather, the speed with which the romance between Steve and Fay develops leaves one with some doubts regarding the depth of their emotions. *Waiting for Lefty,* which also takes place in a relatively constricted time span, is more convincing because all the effects have obviously been developing before the action of the play; the flashbacks make this very clear.

Night Music also departs from the earlier Odets plays in that it obviously de-emphasizes family as a vital force in the development of the play. Truly, it may be argued that Fay Tucker's father comes to New York to see his daughter and to attempt to convince her to return home, but his presence

is not really essential either to the structure of the play or to
the resolution of the conflict. This cannot be said of any of
the earlier plays except, again, *Waiting for Lefty*. *Till the Day
I Die*, while it does not concern itself with the parent-child
relationship as such, does depend upon the relationship of
Ernst Tausig and his brother Carl to demonstrate the complete air of suspicion engendered by the Nazis during Hitler's
regime. If there is any "father" in *Night Music*, it is in the
person of A. L. Rosenberg, who, although unmarried, does
stand as a father surrogate and displays a paternal attitude
and concern for Steve and Fay.

The love relationship between Steve and Fay in *Night Music*
is far more idealized than the same relationships in the other
plays. Florrie and Sid in *Waiting for Lefty* might once have
been like Steve and Fay, but circumstances have combined to
make their love a hopeless thing which, if it found fulfillment in marriage, might degenerate into the sort of relationship which Joe and Edna have. Tilly and Ernst in *Till the
Day I Die* are deeply in love, but their love is secondary to
their party loyalties, which assume the characteristics of fanati-
cism. The idealization of Pearl's love in *Paradise Lost* serves to
embitter rather than enrich the lives of the parties involved
and becomes a destructive force. And Cleo's love in *Rocket
to the Moon* is too generalized to suggest permanence. Odets
used an excellent technique to emphasize the idealization of
the love between Steve and Fay; he superimposed the image
of their pure love upon the background of the infamous Hotel
Algiers. The contrast is striking and the use of secondary
characters to heighten the contrast is especially notable.

Night Music ran a shorter time on Broadway than any other
Odets play. It closed after a disappointing run of only two
weeks. The entire run was overshadowed by numerous unfortunate occurrences. The play opened in Boston and played
to a virtually empty house because of heavy snows and extreme cold during its run. In New York, it opened at the
Broadhurst Theatre, a house which was much too large for
the presentation of a play so intimate as *Night Music*. The
author and Harold Clurman, the director, were not in accord
regarding the interpretation of the play, and the leading man,
Elia Kazan, was admittedly miscast in the role of Steve Takis.

There was very little critical enthusiasm over the production. It was generally admitted that the dialogue was splendid, but there was considerable disagreement about whether the characters were convincing or not. Wolcott Gibbs in his *New Yorker* review said that the characters, ". . . instead of being the sharp, separate, and living creations the author surely imagined them to be, . . . really aren't much more than caricatures." He accused Mr. Odets of engaging ". . . in a lively parody of himself." Joseph Wood Krutch, while admitting that *Night Music* was lively and interesting, felt that it did not represent an advance in the author's development. He called the play "fantastic, episodic, and explosive." He also pointed out that in it Odets had abandoned his usual realism for ". . . a sort of romantic extravaganza." Equally restrained in his comment about the play in *Commonweal*, was Philip T. Hartung, who, while commending ". . . Odets' keen wit and understanding of people," felt that the play was basically inconclusive. In writing of *Night Music* in *New Republic*, Stark Young entitled his critique "Two New Failures," and he justified this judgment of the play by noting that the ". . . wandering, seemingly casual, tangential quality . . . by which it [*Night Music*] meanders along," makes it "50 percent nonsense" in the busy world of 1940. Yet Mr. Clurman points out in his introduction to the Random House edition of the play that it was just this quality which made the critics praise Saroyan's *My Heart's in the Highlands* at about the time that most of them were being very restrained in their praise of Odets.

While Rosamund Gilder saw *Night Music* as the beginning of something very promising in Odets' development, George Jean Nathan expressed himself in *Newsweek* as feeling that "what it [*Night Music*] indicates, and clearly, is . . . a slowly drooping continuance on the lower level of [some] of his antecedent plays." Miss Gilder's hope was based on her feeling that "more than any other writer today he [Odets] is aware of the quality of New York's menacing charivari and is able to record it. The first chords of *Night Music* seemed a prelude to the great play he must some day write on the City of Hope and Fear." *Time's* critic shared with many others the opinion that ". . . the play shows everywhere a slackened rein. It lacks entrails; it lacks sense of direction, it offers no weightier message than that Heaven Helps Those Who Help Themselves."

Few people were able to see in *Night Music* the depth which the author, Mr. Clurman, and the members of the Group Theatre felt the play possessed. Clurman mentions that "Odets takes for granted that we all recognize our homelessness, that we all believe the rootlessness and disorientation of his hero to be typical, that we all know that most of the slogans of our society are without substance in terms of our true emotions." Perhaps Odets gave his audience too much credit in assuming that it would feel as he had hoped.

Only when *Night Music* was revived briefly by the American National Theatre Association in 1951 was it possible to realize the historical importance of the play. Perhaps the greatest praise and understanding bestowed upon it is found in Walter Kerr's review of the presentation which appeared in *Commonweal*. He acknowledged the indebtedness of contemporary playwrights to Odets when he wrote that *Night Music* ". . . serves to remind us that the current—and, I think, hopeful—tendency toward a more poetic realism is really Mr. Odets' invention, and that both Miller and Williams remain indebted to him. . . . Alongside a really striking image, found out of his personal experience and observation, the author would again set an abstract conclusion, a political interpretation. The juxtaposition was embarrassing, as always—in this case more so because of the perspective we acquire on an out-of-date play."

Night Music, more than any other Odets play, combines the tender sweetness of young love with the angry protestation against the pressures imposed by society. The play is more than an inchoate congeries of scenes—as some of the critics would suggest. It is a play which is basically centripetal in its development, as Mr. Krutch has noted, and which, as a result, bewildered the public more than it enlightened it.

III *Clash by Night*

Dissolution was the underlying theme in Clifford Odets' life in the year 1941. His marriage to Luise Rainer ended in divorce during this year and the Group Theatre finally was disbanded. Both occurrences were deeply felt by the author,

for his marriage and his association with the Group Theatre
had, up to this point, represented the two most influential
forces in his life. This was also a year of great international
concern; the bombing of Pearl Harbor by the Japanese on
December 7th marked the entry of the United States into
another world conflict.

When *Clash by Night* opened in New York on December
27, 1941, those who knew Odets expected the new drama to
be pessimistic in tone, and they were not disappointed. Those
who did not know Odets were, notwithstanding the stellar cast,
reluctant to spend an evening seeing a play which had anything to do with a clash; their lives had been filled with clash-
ings on the international front, and they felt in need of light
theatre. The result was that the new play enjoyed only a short
run played before exceptionally sparse audiences.

Clash by Night had a more definite and controlled dramatic
structure than *Night Music* had had. However, *Night Music*
". . . had a more definite theme and far more freshness and
originality in design," according to E. V. R. Wyatt who wrote
of the two plays in *Catholic World.* The only real freshness in
Clash by Night occurs in the subplot involving the two young
people in love, Joe and Peggy, and the handling of this situation is
fresh only in comparison to the main plot, which is the retelling of the time-worn story of a romantic triangle.

Clash by Night had a rather drab cast of characters. The
basic triangle in the play involves Mae Wilenski, a bored wife
and mother who doesn't "happen to care for life on the installment plan."* Her husband is a basically good man who pro-
fesses to worship his wife but is weak and insensitive; and
Earl, the boarder, in the rather drab environment of the Wilenski household takes on a certain glamor engendered solely
by contrast. The inevitable affinity between Mae and Earl
develops; and Odets does not live up to his former promise
because he fails to treat the situation with the special quality
of perception which would lift it above the banality of most
stories based upon a similar situation. David Burnham's obser-
vations in *Commonweal* quite validly asserted that Odets had

Clash by Night, Random House Edition, p. 94. All page references to
Clash by Night will be to this edition.

not given ". . . the familiar situation stature by relating it to
any moral or social standard. Infidelity is meaningless outside
the moral arena. . . . Odets no longer indiscriminately blames
Society, and he doesn't recognize the Devil." This is not to
imply that society does not receive any of the blame for the
situation. The boredom which leads to the dissolution of the
Wilenski marriage stems largely from the economic struggle
which is constantly with the couple; but Odets does not offer
any convincing arguments to justify remedying this situation
on any but the most general humanitarian grounds. Jerry and
Mae Wilenski are just not worthy of any special consideration
in life. They do not appear to have the depth to be able to
sustain any permanent relationship. The passion which causes
Jerry to murder Earl at the end of the play does not appear
to emanate so much from love of Mae as it does from his injured pride.

The only hopeful situation in the play is found in the subplot
involving Joe and Peggy. Like young people in other Odets
plays, this pair has been engaged for nearly two years and
". . . being engaged for nearly two years is no joke in any language!" (13). But this couple, still victims of the Depression,
cannot plan a future when Joe works only three days a week
and makes barely enough money to maintain himself. Society is
indifferent to the fact that Joe is a worthy young man, capable
of meeting difficult situations and of rising to decisive action,
as is shown in his exchange with Kress (212-13). He deserves
much more from life than he is presently able to get. But, as
the play progresses, Joe is shown to be gaining increasing control over his own destiny and the destinies of those about him.
His function in the play seems clearly to be to point towards
a better future. But, as Clurman pointed out in *The Fervent
Years,*

> . . . their presence [that of Peggy and Joe] represented a kind
> of ideologic afterthought rather than the creative center of the
> play, which, no doubt about it, was pessimistic. Odets's feeling
> seemed to be weighed down here by the sense of a working class
> that was basically homeless, racked with inner tension, ignorant,
> baffled, pathetic, and dangerously close to that breaking-point
> of 'mystic' hysteria and violence that often provides the spiritual
> soil for the seeds of fascism.[6]

The social ills which, by breeding insecurity, prevent Joe and Peggy from marrying, are also operative in the other figures in the play, with the possible exception of Earl. This is significant, because Earl does not represent a force for social good, yet he is the most successful person in the play in the materialistic sense of success. Such, Odets would seem to imply, is the situation in a capitalistic society—it is the person who takes what he wants who is the greatest success. But Jerry lives within a conventional moral framework and his existence is overshadowed by the fear that he will find a "pink slip" is his next pay envelope. Mae, of course, shares this fear because she would so fully share the fruits of such a disaster, should it occur. Neither is able to find fulfillment because of the tenuous economic position foisted upon them by the capitalistic system of which they are, of necessity, at one and the same time both the victims and supporters. Because of Jerry's weakness, Mae is more involved in the struggle for existence than might be expected. She objects to this involvement, to this gnawing and perpetual concern, when she tells Earl, "He [Jerry] doesn't know there's a battle of the bread and butter. He expects his wife to fight those battles! He says money isn't everything! I guess the truth is he's a momma's boy . . ." (74).

Perhaps the most tragic figure in the play, although he is not very fully developed, is Jerry's father, who lives with the couple. An immigrant from Poland, he lives in the fear of being sent back to his native country because he never learned to read. He pretends to be able to read and nobody has the humanity to tell him that his position in the United States is secure. Mr. Wilenski is a carpenter who, at an advanced age, still is trying to find work. Since this pursuit is usually for naught, he ". . . plays in bars for drinks. It's the day of rest in his life, an old man . . . he's ashamed" (30). This, then, is the future facing one who has worked hard all his life. In the world's richest country he can look forward only to loneliness, poverty, and almost total social disorientation.

Even though the author is overlooking some of the economic improvements, such as Social Security, which were operative at the time the play was written, he has presented Mr. Wilenski quite well. Odets has used too much restraint in dealing with him; hence, as stated above, the development is not complete. But as a secondary figure, Mr. Wilenski adds immeasurably to the themes of loneliness and social disorientation which pervade the play. His position in a changing world is vividly portrayed. It is clearly evident that the only milieu in which Mr. Wilenski might find identity is in Poland; but the Poland which he left no longer exists and a figure of his sort is just adrift in a world to which he cannot adjust. His isolation is very nearly complete. All the bridges which lead back to his past have been destroyed; all the paths leading to the future terminate, for such as Mr. Wilenski, at an insurmountable wall of stone.

Earl Pfeiffer, although he is in an advantageous economic situation compared with the other characters in the play, presents a dramatic picture of isolation and loneliness. He engages in a steady stream of banter throughout the play, much as Moe Axelrod does in *Awake and Sing!* But Pfeiffer's banter is designed to obscure his real emotions and to assuage the pain of his wife's having left him. His cynicism is a defensive shield erected by him to obscure his basic psychic defeat. He is a more convoluted figure than Moe Axelrod was, and, as a result, he is one of the strongest characters in *Clash by Night*. In spite of the fact that he is despicable in his dealings with the Wilenskis, Earl is a sympathetic figure and the audience is permitted to see him in the round. The Earl who steals another man's wife is the same Earl who buys vitamins for her because he thinks she is run down, or who complains, "I'm always on the outside looking in! . . . I wanna get in somewhere! Someone has to need me, to love me . . . I'm not a barge goin' down the river! . . . The blues for home, for home sweet home, but where is home? Help me, Mae, help me! . . . I'm dying of lonesomeness" (105-6).

Mae, lonely and unable to find what she wants primarily because she has never had a realistic picture of what she might expect from life, is drawn to Earl in his loneliness, but not without acknowledging Jerry's loneliness. She tells Jerry bluntly that their marriage is at an end and says to him, "I know how you feel. Everyone's so goddam lonely! We can't escape that" (188). This is probably the most pessimistic moment in the play. Mae shows pity for Jerry, but tells him, "I can't help you. . . . Don't think I'm heartless, I battered my-self silly not to let this happen. It happened—that's the truth—it happened. . . . We're [Mae and Earl] moving tomorrow" (188). In other words, Odets is admitting the inevitability of loneliness and the impossibility of any real identity and under-standing existing between two people.

Odets uses Vincent Kress, Jerry's uncle, as a spokesman in the play. Similar to Mr. Pike in *Paradise Lost,* his stand is generally less consistent and less conclusive because he is sometimes rightist and sometimes leftist in his sentiments about society. His dialogue is interspersed with Latin because, ac-cording to his own statement, he was trained to be a priest. He is often characterized as a bigot, as when he answers the question of whether he is employed by saying, "Would be if my name was Berkowitz. . . . What's happenin' to this country?" (54).

Kress is helpful in setting the stage for what is to happen and for revealing reactions to situations. For example, when, in the beer-garden scene, Kress's friend, Tom, joins the group Vince points to the dance floor and tells the others, *sotto voce,* "That's his wife dancin' . . . That bag-a-lard in the green dress . . . The gent she's dancin' with—eight thousand bucks an' a Mack truck! . . . He [Tom] knows all about it. They bought him off with pocket change—silver for his pocket!" Jerry's is the only response: "Gee that's a shame . . . golly" (60). This situation, of course, parallels that which is to develop between Mae and Earl; indeed, it is on this very night that Earl, drunk and happy, makes his first obvious advances to Mae who, by this time, has dropped her former reserve and encourages Earl. It is also Kress who plants in Jerry's mind the first seed of suspicion regarding the relationship between Mae and Earl by commenting on how good Earl is to the Wilenski family and saying, "Just spends an' spends an' don't ast nothin' in return, does he? . . . An' yet a little thing like that makes gossip, don't it . . . ?" (133-34).

At times Kress expresses very noble sentiments, but these feelings are expressed in terms so general that it is obvious that what Kress stands for primarily is a form of bigotry which would result in improving his own social standing. When he hears that Earl and Mae are going off together, he is most

indignant and rants that "This is an outrage . . . I'm for reverence, truth an' loyalty . . . so you see. In the new order of
things we'd string his kind up on trees! A great man said it,
social justice for all" (176-77). The new order referred to is
fascist in essence rather than Marxian; and Kress most generally allies himself with this faction in expressing his social
and political philosophies. He would solve problems by "the
whip! Don't the world belong to the strong?" (205). He first
plants in Jerry's mind the thought of meeting his marital
problems by murdering the intruder. Only Joe is able to see
that Kress is "a dangerously ignorant man!" (206-7). To the
others he is an ineffectual eccentric.

One of the minor themes which develops in this play is the
inevitability of conflict. It is a part of life, as demonstrated
by the marital triangle with which the play is ultimately concerned. However, Odets points very gloomily to the apparent
economic necessity for conflict on a larger scale. The dialogue
at this point is filled with social implication:

> JERRY: The buildin' trades is very slow . . . You think
> it's gonna speed up, Joe?
> JOE: If we go to war . . .
> JERRY: I wished you was right, Joe. Then everybody'll
> work.
> PEGGY: You might all get killed, too!
> JOE: We might . . .
> JERRY: . . . You are just in the world on a rain check,
> as I see it. Nobody knows what'll happen next. Every-
> thing boils down to worry . . . nobody don't sleep a whole
> night's sleep no more.
>
> (126-27)

Joe speaks with a resignation born of despair. He is part
of a consuming industrial complex, too big to comprehend,
which may demand his life; but until it makes this demand, it
sustains him; he therefore cannot question the validity of its
existence.

Perhaps the major weakness of *Clash by Night* is that the
play is concerned more with the results of the social forces
which determine the lives of the characters than with their
causes and remedies. Such might also be said, though less

generally, of *Rocket to the Moon;* in both plays the results are given much more thorough consideration than the causes. Directly in contrast is a play such as *Waiting for Lefty* in which the causes are minutely examined and in which the remedy is shouted out at an aroused audience in the words, "Strike, strike, strike!" The audience could leave a performance of *Waiting for Lefty* with the feeling that the social action implied by the play had direction and force. The ending of *Clash by Night* is utterly without forward motion. The future is clear. Jerry is a murderer and Mae is a woman who has absolutely no place to turn.

Because of the grave international situation at the time of its presentation, *Clash by Night* received less critical attention than any other major Odets play. The reviews which were written were almost unanimous in feeling that the play was a disappointment. However, nearly all of the reviewers re-acted favorably to the presentation of the dialogue and to the development of the characters. Wolcott Gibbs, writing a most unfavorable criticism in *The New Yorker,* had to admit that "now and then a symptom of Mr. Odets' real talent comes through— a true and memorable line, something acutely observed and accurately reported." David Burnham felt that Odets had chosen an adequate frame of reference for his earlier plays when his concern was with the class struggle, but that all that carried over from this into the present play was a "hu-manitarian intuition of the individual's private separation, which is valid background for pathos but not for tragedy."[7] John Gassner, who recognized little more than good intentions in *Clash by Night,* wrote in *Theatre Arts Monthly* that "good writing went to waste as Odets invited obtuseness with his fable of adultery, and skepticism by the earnestness with which he sought to impose significance on the banal plot." Miss Wyatt, the reviewer for *Catholic World,* objected that "some of the dialogue is an unnecessary challenge to decency."

No play could have appeared at a less fortunate time his-torically than *Clash by Night* did. However, the fact remains that the play was inherently weak in many respects; indeed, it is doubtful that it would have enjoyed any greater success than it did had it appeared at a less crucial time.

IV *The Middle Span*

The three plays which serve to represent the middle span in Clifford Odets' career as playwright are more specifically subjective than are his first five plays. They represent his own uncertainties and frustrations during the most difficult period in his life. They may be interpreted in terms of the broader general social meanings implicit in them, but basically these plays are most convincing as dramas which are more deeply concerned with individual problems than with the problems of the social mass. This statement is true partially because, with the correction of some of the social ills which had aroused Odets in the 1930's, he found himself a rebel with no pressing cause, and made the compromise of writing about moribund causes as though they were still vital and timely. Only in *Night Music* does his viewpoint approach what might be called a hopeful stand. The future, on both the individual and broadly social levels, is quite grim in both *Rocket to the Moon* and *Clash by Night*.

In all of those later plays, there is a basic concern with the problems of love and marriage; and the old concern with childlessness is still very much in evidence, as is that of man's inability to marry because of economic uncertainty. However, the concern with the family as a basic social unit is less apparent in these plays than it was in such early dramas as *Awake and Sing!, Paradise Lost,* and *Golden Boy.*

Odets has not, in *Rocket to the Moon,* and *Clash by Night,* lost sight of the fundamental role which economics plays in determining the course of human existence. There is always present in the plays the implication that life would cease to be such a worrisome problem if the capitalistic system were replaced by a more egalitarian economic and political system. Since the validity of such a concept is extremely dubious, the author might justly be accused of having found in it an overly simple and ineffective solution to a very complex, multifaceted problem.

A very early unpublished one-act play by Odets, entitled *Remember* and concerned with the horrors of relief, shows very clearly the danger of escape into emotion if it leads one away from the realities of basic problems. Yet it would seem that in these three plays of the late 1930's and early 1940's, Odets had ignored many of the realities of the problems he was dealing with; and, in so doing, had lost, to a degree, the vitality and vigor which had caused him to be heralded as "the white hope of the thirties."

CHAPTER 5

The Locust and the Peach

"There is idealism
in just survival."
(From *The Flowering Peach*)

CLIFFORD ODETS spent the years following *Clash by Night* writing motion picture scenarios in Hollywood. He was not to produce another stage play until 1948, when he finished working on *A Winter Journey;* renamed *The Big Knife,* it reached Broadway early in 1949. This play was followed in 1950 by *The Country Girl,* and in 1954 by *The Flowering Peach.*

Odets' years in the film industry had brought about very noticeable changes in him. If *Waiting for Lefty* and *Till the Day I Die* had reflected the vigorous anger of his youth, and if *Rocket to the Moon* and *Clash by Night* had revealed a cynicism not evident in the younger Odets, then surely *The Big Knife* gave evidence, first, of an Odets who had grown immeasurably in dramatic technique and, second, of an Odets who was proving himself sufficiently versatile to write with as much feeling about problems of the well-to-do as, fifteen years earlier, he had written of the problems of those who were oppressed through poverty. *The Country Girl* represented, in many respects, a continuation of the promise found in *The Big Knife.* The play dealt superficially with theatrical life, but more deeply with the effects of alcoholism and insecurity. The hero, Frank Elgin, is grappling with the problems of conquering his alcoholism so that he may make a comeback as an actor. The play is basically concerned with the deep and complicated insecurities which face him and over which he must gain control.

When it appeared that Odets had settled into a pattern of writing plays about show business and the people in it, he surprised his public and the critics. At the same time, he gave further evidence of his versatility with the presentation of *The Flowering Peach,* a warm and humorous allegory based on the biblical account of Noah and the flood. This play reached Broadway in December, 1954, and ran for some four months. Odets is presently hopeful that he will be able to produce alternately film plays and stage plays. He recently was quoted by the *New York Herald Tribune* as saying with assurance and genuine conviction, "My best plays are ahead."

I *The Big Knife*

In a statement to the press in 1938, Mr. Odets said that ". . . acting is a whorish thing." What he meant becomes fully clear in *The Big Knife,* a play which chronicles the events in the life of a highly successful actor who ultimately commits suicide. This actor, Charlie Castle, is one of the leading cinema idols in the country and, as such, is worth millions of dollars to the studio which holds his contract. Marcus Hoff, a motion-picture tycoon, is determined that Charlie shall sign with his studio and has had an unprecedented contract drawn up offering the actor nearly four million dollars for his services during the next fourteen years and offering him, also, the right to reject any scripts which he does not deem worthy of his talents.

But Charlie does not wish to sign such a contract because his wife Marion, who is now living apart from him, vows that she will not return if he makes such a commitment. However, a simple refusal to sign is not possible; for Marcus Hoff is blackmailing Charlie, threatening that if he does not accept the contract, he will make public the fact that Charlie is responsible for a hit-and-run death for which his publicity man, Buddy Bliss, out of friendship for Charlie, took the responsibility and subsequently served time in prison. Because of his fear of this revelation Charlie finally signs the contract; but, having signed it, he cannot live with himself. He comes to realize that he is little more than a chattel. His self-respect has been sold for a price, and without self-respect Charlie cannot face himself. He does the only thing left for him to do; he slashes his wrists and dies.

Odets' identification with Charlie Castle is very obvious in many instances throughout the play. Castle, like Odets, had read Victor Hugo and, in the play, he states that ". . . Hugo's the one who helped me nibble my way through billions of polly seeds. Sounds grandiose, but Hugo said to me: 'Be a good boy, Charlie. Love people, do good, help the lost and fallen, make the world happy, if you can!' "* Stated with simplicity, this was the ideal by which Charlie Castle desired to live; it was his awareness of the gap between his ideal and the reality of his life which caused him to be essentially a weakling and an escapist—a man who, in his mid-thirties, could look forward to very little except the forgetfulness which he found in an overindulgence in liquor.

Actually, Charlie had accepted fame in exchange for his manhood. He had become an object to be haggled over, to be lent out, to be subdivided, just as Joe Bonaparte had become such an object in *Golden Boy*. His loss of identity, first engineered by the studio, which made him change his name from Cass to Castle, increases with the action of the play. His recognition of this loss of identity is fully realized when, in conversation with a neighbor, Charlie says, "I'll bet you don't know why we all wear these beautiful, expensive ties in Hollywood. . . . It's a military tactic—we hope you won't notice our faces" (106).

Charlie, at the acme of success in his profession, has reached his nadir as a man; he is not in control of his own destiny. He can never act naturally, never speak frankly, because someone is always watching and listening; someone is always eager to help lead the great man to his downfall. He tells his wife that "free speech is the highest-priced luxury in this country today" (16). Charlie must, in this atmosphere, have his thoughts shaped for him and must yield his ideals utterly to the forces which have brought about his success. He has no choice but to make an amoeba-like adaptation to the sort of life which is now inevitable for him. He must pay heed to the words of Marcus Hoff's toady, Smiley Coy, who advises him, "Don't

*The Big Knife, Random House Edition, p. 9. All subsequent references to the play shall be to this edition.

study life—get used to it" (81). It is in such casual statements as this that one finds Odets' most cutting, most subjective criticism of the film industry.

Only in *Till the Day I Die* and in *Golden Boy* has Odets produced such a clearly defined and fully delineated central character as Charlie Castle. In *Waiting for Lefty* there was no single central character; rather, the working class emerged as hero. In *Awake and Sing!* and in *Paradise Lost*, the emergent character was a composite family character. In the plays dealing with love, the emphasis was not on a single character. However, *The Big Knife* revolves around Charlie Castle, who, peculiarly enough, is probably the weakest character in the play. The only thing which makes him central is that he can make money for his studio. Marcus Hoff can use Charlie as a means towards making millions. Buddy Bliss and Dixie Evans are both attracted to Charlie because of the position which Hoff has given him. Charlie, as an individual, does not assume any overwhelming proportions in the play, hence it can be only a false Hollywood glamor, contrived by the studio, which draws people to him. Even the kindly Nat Danziger has no deep intrinsic feeling for Charlie. He is, of necessity, involved with him in business dealings, and his nature is so obviously outgoing and humanitarian that he does all in his power to give Charlie the kindly counsel of which he stands in need; however, Odets does not give the reader cause to suppose that Nat could have become Charlie's friend through any natural affinity.

Marion Castle's relationship to her husband also boils down essentially to a matter of economics. Marion, the daughter of a noted history professor, has always known security and been socially above Charlie, whose background is sketched in at the beginning of the play when, in telling about his uncle, he says, "He merely raised me when my parents died. . . . They were awfully poor, my aunt and uncle. I made money too late to be able to help them. I regret that" (9). The cultural gap between the two is re-emphasized throughout the play in various incidental ways, as when Marion asks Charlie, "Why do you keep using words like 'ain't'?" (60).

Marion, because of her inborn security, something which Charlie will never be able to attain, is essentially a fearless person. Audacious enough to tell Patty Benedict, the gossip columnist, to mind her own business, she also stands her ground with Marcus Hoff, one of the most powerful men in Hollywood, when she says, "Mr. Hoff, can't you stop talking about yourself?" (124). To Charlie, who is very much in love with her, she represents all that is not Hollywood. Hank Teagle characterized the relationship between them very well when he said to Charlie, "I know that Marion stands in your life for idealism . . . and that you've wounded her and it" (109). Charlie cannot deny this. It is clear to him that, just as their expected child has been killed by an abortion, so has his idealism been annihilated by the false and destructive values which he had to accept as the price of success in Hollywood.

Odets' most direct criticism of Hollywood is found in *The Big Knife*. Hollywood is depicted as the place of "sin" which Odets had called it some years earlier. Even as the play opens, the venomous Patty Benedict gives a vivid insight into Hollywood's social attitudes:

> PATTY: I like the airiness of this room. . . . French paintings, dear one?
> CHARLIE: Yeah.
> PATTY: Don't you buy American any more?
> CHARLIE: . . . I don't know one painter from another. . . . I wouldn't want my fans to say I've gone arty, would I?
>
> (6)

Because Patty is a widely read columnist, and because she is basically so warped and unwholesome, every question she asks must be answered with extreme caution. She is to be fenced with rather than talked to. Her question—"Don't you buy American any more?"—is an irrelevant and unfair one. Charlie's answer, while a safe one, is also characteristic: the implication is obviously that the buyers of paintings are more prestige-conscious than artistically aware. Finally Charlie admits in this bit of dialogue that he must live and act constantly in the shadow of what his fans are likely to think of him; for him to admit a proclivity towards one of the finer aspects of human endeavor would be damaging to him professionally.

There seems in this situation to be an echo of the central conflict of *Golden Boy;* but the deeper conflict is the one within the author who is faced with the problems of writing what is within him, or of producing popular films which he knows to be of limited artistic value. Down to the present time, Odets has not completely solved the problem of merging his artistic integrity with practical necessity, and the question of how to meet both the artistic and practical needs in his life is still one of his major personal problems. Marion speaks directly of this conflict when she tells Charlie that "Your sin is living against your own nature. You're denatured—that's your sin!" (62). But by this time Charlie is so far removed from his real nature that he can no longer be said to have one. He has lost his personality; life has eroded his ideals to such a point that the only thing that remains of him is his likeness on a kiosk. His life is one of constant retreat.

The insincerity of Hollywood is a major factor in bringing about Charlie's disillusionment. The film magnates who stoop to blackmailing him are the very people who profess adoration of him. Charlie, disgusted after having been forced into signing his fourteen-year contract, very tellingly says, "The free giving of hearts out here begins to freeze my blood" (47). His eyes are open to the real Hollywood: the Hollywood which can pay a man a thousand dollars a week for four years and not even ". . . remember his name or what he wrote" (114); the Hollywood which can ponder over how a man is able to live so well ". . . on four thousand a week" (36-37).

In writing a critique of life in Hollywood, Odets has not departed so far from his original interests and ideals as many of his critics would have one believe. One must remember Odets' statement: "All of my plays . . . deal with one subject; the struggle not to have life nullified by circumstances, false values, anything." All of Odets' plays have been concerned with the problems brought about by the effect of mendacity on a broad social situation. In *The Big Knife* he has chosen to write of a level of society with which he had not previously concerned himself, and many critics viewed this as a weakness, as a retreat from the social problems which were at the heart of the earlier Odets plays. But who is to limit the playwright in this way? It must be remembered that Charlie Cass came from the same sort of background which Odets had been writing about in his earlier plays and from which Odets himself had come. The play is concerned with the effect of a notably false society upon a person who, by circumstances, is forced into it. Odets is able to write of this problem with feeling and conviction because of his intimate personal association with it.

Charlie ultimately is forced into committing suicide because his life has ceased to have any meaning. Hollywood has nullified all of the challenge which his life had held during the early days of his marriage when he and Marion had struggled to eke out an existence in New York. In addressing Hank Teagle, Charlie makes his desperation quite clear:

> And do you say in your book it isn't even easy to go to hell today? That there's nothing left to sin against? . . . Correction! There's health left to sin against! Health—the last, nervous conviction of the time! We're sick at heart, but we'll increase the life span! What for? Nobody knows! . . . You're right, Hank. Your hero's half a man, neither here nor there, dead from the gizzard up. Stick him with a pin and see, psst! No feelings! When I came home from Germany . . . I saw most of the war dead were here, not in Africa and Italy. And Roosevelt was dead . . . and we plunged ourselves, all of us, into the noble work of making the buck reproduce itself!
>
> (111)

But even more telling is a statement in the very last minute of the play. Charlie, speaking to Marion, says, "You see, everyone needs a cause to touch greatness" (137). This statement reveals a great deal about Charlie, but even more about Odets.

The Big Knife was received in New York with great interest and mixed feelings. John Gassner indicated that since Odets' rise to prominence, only two young writers, Tennessee Williams and Arthur Miller, had written with such animation. Certainly the force of this animation is felt in such a scene as that in which Charlie is feeling remorseful because of the problems which he has caused Nat, his agent. He says, "Why did I add this burden to that grotesque, devoted soul? Did you ever notice? He moves his lips when he reads" (136). This sort of acute and revealing observation reminds one of the careful artistry of a Rembrandt who so fully caught the nuances of his characters' expressions that he made them seem alive. In another scene, Marion says that ". . . to be faithful . . . gives you that loony, old-fashioned moral grandeur of an equestrian statue in the park" (25). This sort of keen observation and expression has helped to establish Odets as a foremost American playwright.

Writing in *School and Society*, William H. Beyer, after calling *The Big Knife* ". . . bitter, angry, diffused, and garrulous diatribe, a sprawling melodrama of the sinister ways of Hollywood," admits that "in the lesser characters . . . Mr. Odets has given us some sharp, compelling characterizations." However, Beyer did not feel that *The Big Knife* represented a step forward for Odets, and he called the play contrived. Miss Wyatt of the *Catholic World* called the play a "Hollywood nightmare," and looked upon it as a purge for the author, who, she hoped, would go on to write a really excellent play. Wolcott Gibbs, writing in *The New Yorker*, labeled the play ". . . an enormous commotion"; he was disappointed at not finding in it a suggestion of more universal moral implications.

Possibly the most just and balanced evaluation of *The Big Knife* was that written by Kappo Phelan in *Commonweal*. While she was not entirely pleased with the play, she admitted that ". . . the astonishing rhetoric Clifford Odets has welded to his astonishing plot in this particular performance is almost indescribable." She gives a perspicacious estimate of Odets when she writes, "It would seem, adding his promotion to his history, that he [Odets] is angry about his position in our society: a position of a man who thinks to the left and at the same time is holding jobs as far to the right as possible." She makes what seems a legitimate criticism in objecting to the fact that the catastrophe of the play is presented in talk rather than in action.

Most of the criticism of the play dealt with specifics and with the immediate story of the play. As a result, some of the significant, far-reaching implications were lost. Brooks Atkinson pointed out that ". . . one of Mr. Odets' virtues [is] that he always tries to write on the high plane of dramatic art, and he has the talent to do so." Some critics lost sight of this fact, even though Odets himself had said that ". . . essentially it [*The Big Knife*] dealt with the tragedy of lost integrity everywhere."

II *The Country Girl*

It has been suggested that *The Country Girl* may have been merely a slick potboiler, written by Odets for commercial reasons. Indeed, the author himself stated that the play was without a very serious message and aimed merely to present ". . . certain small aspects of life—and I hope reality." In a recent review, the author accounted for the adroit glibness of the play by saying, ". . . I picked up half my technique here [in Hollywood]. I did . . . [a number of] movies before I wrote *Country Girl*. The movies are a brilliant training school for a dramatic writer." This statement surely seems to be a reasonable explanation of his change in style, and it also represents a rather dramatic reversal of his earlier opinions regarding the effect of Hollywood upon a dramatic talent.

The Country Girl underwent a great deal of revision after the author had set down his initial version. He claims to have written two or three versions of the play before showing it to anyone. His revisions consisted mainly in the ". . . rewriting of certain scenes pertaining to the dramatic structure. I didn't know until the second draft, for example, that Georgie wasn't a destructive, bitchy woman." The play seems, on the surface, to be a psychological study of the actor, Frank Elgin, an alcoholic who is attempting to make a comeback on the stage, and of his effect upon his wife Georgie, and upon his director Bernie Dodd.

Frank, who suffers from a deep and well-established sense of insecurity, has strong paranoid tendencies. He struggles to give the appearance of being easygoing and happy; however, in doing so, he is merely playing a role. His wife realizes this and she explains him to Bernie very acutely when she says, "He doesn't like to make the slightest remark that might lose him people's regard or affection."*

However, despite this surface indication that *The Country Girl* is primarily a psychological play, it is not consistently so. Odets claimed to be trying to combine ". . . a certain linear drive of story with psychological drive." In doing so, he often

---

*The Country Girl, Acting Edition, p. 41. All subsequent references will be to this edition.

tended to become more concerned with the social than with the psychological elements of the play. Throughout the drama, Odets, as Harold Clurman has noted, ". . . constantly asks, 'What helps a man to live?' 'What today injures man's spirit?' 'What enhances or diminishes the creatively human in him?' " When Odets comes to grips with these questions, he answers them in terms of social rather than purely psychological forces. Obviously, these terms are not mutually exclusive; Frank's drinking stems from his insecurity which is, in this case, a psychological problem. However, it was brought about by social forces, by the uncertainty of an actor's existence, by the poverty which kept Frank at a bare subsistence level for the ten years during which he was unable to find any employment aside from small parts or an occasional role as an understudy. When Frank finally regains his confidence and shows signs of conquering his problems, he does so because he has gained social approval, because he is once more being applauded as the great actor who had previously gained widespread recognition and acclaim.

Had *The Country Girl* been more exclusively a psychological play, it is doubtful that Odets could have changed the role of Georgie so drastically in the various versions of the script. Had Georgie been presented as the nagging wife, as she had been conceived by Odets earlier, Frank's weakness would have been pitiful and psychologically understandable and explicable. But in the final version of the play, Frank's weakness is understandable only on social grounds and, in essence, Odets' implications are not markedly different from those in his earlier proletarian plays. Frank's psychological composition is relatively transparent; the social forces which have engendered the actor's psychological problems are delineated with much more restraint than are the purely psychological forces; but they become a strong underlying theme in the overall structure of the play.

The Country Girl cannot really be said to have more than two significant characters in it. Georgie and Frank are well developed; but the six remaining characters, with the possible exception of Bernie, never really come to life, nor does Odets show evidence of any real interest in them. Cook, the producer, is a stereotype of a businessman who is looking out for his investment. He is edgy, insensitive to the feelings of others, dynamic in his actions. He is capable of giving encouragement only to someone whose worth has been proved and publicly acclaimed. When Frank most needs encouragement, it is consistent with Cook's personality that he should pounce on him as he does, saying, "Well, this does it! . . . That wife of yours can help you start packing!" (60). It is only when Frank has evoked unrestrained and unprecedented applause from the New York audience that Cook can say, "Frank, a lot of things . . . are said in the heat and toil of the day. I hope you'll accept my apologies" (73). And then he admits that he is attempting to make peace with Frank only because he has in mind some new contractual arrangements. Cook is not significantly different in personality from Tom Moody in *Golden Boy* or from Marcus Hoff in *The Big Knife*. However, his character is so barely sketched in, that one finds it difficult to feel any strong emotions for or against him.

Paul Unger, the author of the play in which Frank is to make his return to the theatre, is quietly intelligent, sensitive, sympathetic. Though he is generally very complacent, he can rise to action when goaded into doing so. When Cook abuses Frank, it is Unger who, whitefaced and angry, tells him, "You're the boss, Mr. Cook, but you can't talk that way to an actor in any show I'm on. I won't permit it" (60). Paul represents the voice of social conscience heard in so much of Odets' work; but this voice is somewhat hushed in *The Country Girl*. The author does not give it the opportunity to expostulate at length as in the earlier plays. He is free to admit that ". . . in *The Country Girl* my point of view was held in abeyance." *Time's* review of the play pointed out that "the real story . . . is a compact little tragedy of misunderstanding." There is social protest in the play, but it is intimated rather than frankly stated. Although there is probably no single reason for this, one cannot ignore the fact that in the years following World War II congressional committees were very active in their investigations of literary works of social protest. Such writers as Albert Maltz and Ring Lardner, Jr., were taken into custody and questioned about their political philosophies. The year 1950 was not one in which an author could safely criticize existing social institutions in any but an indirect manner.

Nancy Stoddard, the eighteen-year-old actress who is to play opposite Frank in Unger's play, is presented very sketchily and never is seen as a total personality. However, she is very useful in the play because Frank's reactions to her illustrate significant facets of his own personality. Early in the play, when Frank and the company of Unger's play are in the theatre rehearsing, Frank forgets his lines. Nancy, who has already memorized all the parts in the play, prompts him; and Frank, looking grumpily at her, cautions, "Never usurp the stage manager's position, dear. Older actors don't like it" (22). As the play continues, Frank, because of his basic insecurity, tends to use Nancy as a scapegoat. When he mixes up his lines, he hastens to say to Bernie, ". . . that line mixup—it was the kid's fault all the time!" (42). Frank is jealous of Nancy's youth and of her acting ability; she constantly serves to remind him of what he might have been had he had more stability. She makes him painfully aware of his own inadequacies, inadequacies of which he needs no reminder. When he tells Georgie that ". . . the whole company—none of them like me. . . . They all want me to fail!" (57-58), his defenses are down; his paranoia is evident. However, when his defenses are not down, his paranoia becomes evident in other ways, and his abuse of Nancy is obviously a manifestation of his psychological condition.

Nancy finally becomes instrumental in helping Frank to gain the inner security which he requires in order to make his comeback. As he is playing opposite her, he forgets that he is playing a role and begins to live his part. He strikes out and slaps Nancy repeatedly until she makes a hysterical exit. The curtain falls and the audience, for the first time since the play has opened, gives its tumultuous acclaim to Frank's performance. It is at this moment that Frank begins to regain his self-confidence; his past is behind him and he is now going to be able to rise above it. When Georgie had said, "People don't go back" (49), Frank was filled with doubt about his future. But now he knows that his direction will be as he willed it. At the same time, his human relationships will change because, with success, he will be less inclined to feel that the world is against him. His relentless striking of Nancy marked a turning point in his life. Into this act went all of his pent-up bitterness.

In *The Country Girl*, man's ego is studied carefully and the effect of the wounded ego upon man's total situation is explored. Elements of this problem have been studied and presented forcefully in other Odets plays; however, in none of his earlier plays has Odets been so fully concerned with the problem, nor has he so sharply focused his interest upon a single character. Jacob, in *Awake and Sing!*, suffered a great wound to his ego during his later years, and his suicide was an outgrowth of this wound. The wounded ego was again dealt with in *Night Music*, but, for Steve Takis, suicide was not a solution; instead Steve grew in strength and, as the play closed, was much more in control of his own destiny than he had been when the play opened. It is on a similar hopeful note that *The Country Girl* concludes.

The tension in the play is largely the result of the interaction of the personalities of Frank and Georgie. Each tends to blame the other for the disappointment which characterizes his life. Frank, unable to admit that it is his own weakness which has made him an alcoholic, fabricates a story which places the blame on Georgie. He tells of her violent acts when he has had to leave her alone to act in plays; but, in so doing, he is simply imputing to her his own tendencies. He excuses his drinking by calling attention to the fact that Georgie, too, was a drinker, but that when he starts drinking, she stops. He lies about Georgie's past when he tells Bernie that she was "Miss America" in the late 1930's. The motivation for this lie is obviously Frank's desire to enhance his own prestige by showing that a "Miss America" could fall in love with him. He introduces a note of tragedy into their lives when he tells of the child which they lost in the 1940's; his implication is that this unhappy event caused their social and spiritual decline. Only by losing himself in fantasy can Frank bear to think of what his life has been. The lies about his past become so real for him that they cease to be lies at all.

Odets, in depicting Frank as he does, is dealing with mendacity in individual terms rather than on a more broadly social level such as one might note in such earlier works as *Paradise Lost* and *Awake and Sing!* In all of the earlier plays, as well as in *The Big Knife*, the author was concerned with the false standards which society imposes upon man. Men were depicted as being the victims of the socio-economic milieu in which they found themselves. *Rocket to the Moon* and *Clash by Night* present mendacity on a more individual level than is found in the earlier plays, but the characters of these two plays lie to each other more than to themselves. In each of these plays there is a romantic triangle; in each there is the deception generally made necessary by such a situation. But in the play at hand, the leading character is involved in a self-deception of such proportions that truth and fantasy have merged in his own thinking. It is for this reason, perhaps, that he is such an effective actor; he can live most convincingly the life of the fictitious character whom he is portraying; when he begins slapping Nancy during a performance, he turns in a brilliant performance, but, at the same time, relieves his personal animosity towards the girl.

Despite outward appearances, Frank is introverted. His drinking has tended to shut the world out of his life. Even though he realizes what the consequences of his weakness might be for him and his wife, he cannot exist without the stimulation of alcohol. He buys cough medicine with a high alcoholic content and uses it in place of liquor until Georgie takes it from him. Especially tense is the scene in which she confiscates the cough medicine and nags him to reveal the location of the other bottle which she is sure he has hidden nearby. Frank lies to her very convincingly, but the moment she leaves the room, he pulls from the bottom of his trunk the bottle which he has placed there. Living with the shame and full realization of his own failure and weakness, Frank has had no choice but to withdraw into himself. He has not the strength to do otherwise. Only as the play closes has anyone cause to suppose that Frank might find the strength to mend his broken life.

However, Odets does not attempt to give an explicit answer to the question of whether a person who has lived so selfishly and who has such extreme weakness of character to contend with can be redeemed simply by having his one great talent recognized. Viewing Frank as objectively as possible, one would be forced to admit that the chances of his personality's undergoing any real transformation would be very slight indeed. Frank is actually unable to grow up. He represents, as much as any Arthur Miller or Tennessee Williams protagonist, the prototype of the failure of modern American man. He is insensitive to his wife's need for inner security, and her total effort is directed towards humoring him and looking after him. The major question is whether Frank is worth this sacrifice.

Georgie's marriage to Frank is not fully explained by Odets. Presumably she was overwhelmed by his charm and by the glamor which attended his early theatrical successes. Georgie is completely aware of the amount of responsibility which she is shouldering in her marriage and she often tends to look upon herself as a martyr. Apparently she had hoped, in marrying Frank who was so much older than she, to find a father-husband. Indeed, she tells of her loneliness as a child during the long periods when her father was on the road in vaudeville, and says to Frank, "[I] might not have married you if I'd had a father" (33). She goes on to tell Frank that he does not believe in himself, but her attempt to dominate him so completely results in his being deprived of any opportunity to be independent. She is not entirely culpable in this, however; Frank has not the self-control and will power which enable a man to stand alone. Her motivation in being overly protective of Frank is, in all fairness, basically selfless. Her marriage has been disappointing because Frank is unable to assume the role of leadership which Georgie has convinced herself she wants her husband to assume. She cannot even get Frank to make relatively simple decisions, because he is always afraid of hurting her. She says to him, at one point, ". . . come on, Frank, tell me what you want me to do. I won't love you less. . . . If I go on the road with you . . . tell me straight out anything that's on your mind. Don't shuffle" (33).

This is Georgie's self-created illusion of what she would have her husband be. However, were Frank to take command of the situation, Georgie would be thoroughly miserable. She has assumed a protective role and, in a sense, her relationship to Frank is more that of mother than that of wife. It is for this reason that Georgie, contrary to the behavior of the average woman, frequently makes allusions to the fact that she is old. When Nancy calls a mirror a pier-glass, Georgie says that ". . . only old ladies like me" (49) still use that terminology. Actually, Georgie is in her thirties and is represented as being quite attractive.

Georgie's protectiveness, the result of misplaced maternal feelings, has virtually emasculated Frank. Any hope which might exist for him is contingent upon his getting away from her overpowering influence upon him. As the play closes, there is not any indication that Frank is to gain this liberation. Indeed, Odets, in an interview, indicated that ". . . the action is resolved by Georgie sticking with Frank and Bernie going off alone. But the real interpretation of what will happen to these people is for the reader or audience [to decide upon]." Odets considers this ending the best technical job he has ever done.[1]

The critical reception of *The Country Girl* was notably varied. It ranged from Brooks Atkinson's estimate that ". . . *The Country Girl* is the best play he [Odets] has written for years, perhaps the best play of his career," to George Jean Nathan's comment in *American Mercury* that "he [Odets] is theatrical not in the sense of true theatre, but in the sense of falsified stage." Basic disagreement over specific points characterized much of the criticism of the play. For example, William Beyer wrote in *School and Society* that ". . . the opening scene of the actor's try-out reading is so labored and perfunctory both in its concept and in its execution that we were immediately apprehensive as to the play's development." On the other hand, Miss Wyatt wrote in *Catholic World*, "Act I holds the most interest."

All but a few critics considered the play to be generally a sound technical achievement. Margaret Marshall, reviewing the play for *Nation*, wrote, "The play is well made. Mr. Odets knows the language and ways of the theatre. He also knows how to build a scene and how to induce a rising tension. . . . The situation, if small, is interesting." *Time* considered Odets' characters in the play to be "bitingly real" and noted that the play had ". . . passages of fierce feeling that only Odets could write." The reviewer for *Commonweal*, Walter Kerr, called the play ". . . well balanced [with] passages of quiet, careful motivation . . . followed by inevitable and satisfying flareups; nothing is tacked on; everything moves with easy confidence." It is this architectonic quality which makes *The Country Girl* a technically sound achievement.

Few critics have written of the play with the perspicacity of John Mason Brown. In his review in the *Saturday Review*, he recognized *The Country Girl* as a competent play, and he realized that "Odets' career got off to a poor start in starting too well. It began with a climax." Only the critic for *Newsweek* could see in *The Country Girl* ". . . a strictly theatrical piece with the same vigor and dramatic skill that he [Odets] once dedicated to causes and social significance."

The most widely acclaimed strength of the play was Odets' presentation of Frank and Georgie. *Life* called them ". . . almost too excruciatingly real to watch, but too absorbing to ignore." Harold Clurman, whose criticism of the play Odets felt to be most significant, praised the author's ". . . talent for living dramatic speech, for characterization, for intensity of feeling."[2] He went on to call Odets a poet of the theatre and noted his ability to write with immediacy and intimacy. But, most important of all, Clurman said that Odets previous successes had been bold revolutionary plays, but that their success had been ". . . partly due to the mood of the thirties and our foolish appetite for novelty." In this statement, Clurman seems to have come to the heart of the matter; those who had criticized Odets for abandoning his soapbox were the very critics who would have condemned him for lacking versatility had he continued to write the sort of plays that the 1930's demanded. Odets, in the 1940's and 1950's, moved from dead themes which had ceased to have meaning to those he considered more vital and timely.

In *The Country Girl*, Odets had set as his task ". . . to take simple elements and make something sharp and theatrical out of them. I stated a fact, the story of these people, rather than speculated a fact."[3] The play accomplished the author's basic aim and the public received it well. As a motion picture it also enjoyed a modicum of success. But more important than anything else, *The Country Girl* gives evidence not only that Odets' social commentary can be expressed in a more restrained manner than had hitherto been evident in his works, but also that this restraint did not result from a weakening social concern. It came from a broadening of his interest in the matters which vitally affect man in his social relationships.

III *The Flowering Peach*

The Flowering Peach, produced in New York in December, 1954, marks a departure from Clifford Odets' previous plays both in scope and in style of presentation. Deeply allegorical,

CLIFFORD ODETS

The Flowering Peach is a retelling of the story of Noah and the Ark, freely adapted from the Book of Genesis. The play might be called a modern retelling of the story; the dialogue is modern, many of the situations are presented in a modern context, and the men dress in modern clothing. However, the women are clothed in traditional Oriental costumes, and the author's desire seems to be to create a feeling of timelessness which would tend to give the play a greater universality.

The Flowering Peach is Odets' most poetic and most highly imaginative play. The characters are lovable and convincing; the allegory is constantly present, but not intrusive; the humor is light, natural, and pervasive. Long before Odets had thought of writing *The Flowering Peach*, Harold Clurman had observed that ". . . he is never literal and his power with words [represents] a blood tie with the sources."[4] It is Odets' blood tie with his sources that makes *The Flowering Peach* a genuine artistic triumph. To the traditional story of Noah and the Ark, Odets brings a deep understanding of Jewish family life. He captures the warmth of the family much as he had in *Awake and Sing!* and in *Paradise Lost*. His approach has shifted from the almost clinically objective point of view of *The Country Girl;* in *The Flowering Peach*, it becomes warmly subjective.

Odets' blood tie with his sources in *The Country Girl* was found in his prolonged association with the theatre; his blood tie in *The Flowering Peach* is represented by his continued concern with the family as the fundamental unit of society—a concern equally prominent in his earlier, more angry writings. But in *The Flowering Peach* Odets has become mellow. If, in *Awake and Sing!* he could have a perturbed Jacob say, "This is a house? Marx said it—abolish such families," then the matriarchal Esther in *The Flowering Peach*, upon discovering that her son Shem has almost sunk the Ark by hoarding manure in his quarters, can have the compassion to say, as Bessie Berger might have, "But if it's for the family, why throw it overboard?"*
Esther is able to bear the confinement of the Ark, the un-

The Flowering Peach as reproduced in *The Best Plays of 1954-55*, ed. Louis Kronenberger, p. 197. All subsequent references will be to this edition of the play.

certainty of the future, the constant bickering among the members of her family, because the family is together and this, to her, is the most significant satisfaction she can envision.

The family becomes the symbol of regeneration, of stolid continuance in the face of the most frightening and widespread adversity, represented by the flood. This symbol is reinforced as the play concludes; the women who have been aboard the Ark—Rachel, Leah, and Goldie—are great with children when the waters recede. The repopulation of the earth is to begin. Noah sees a tree blossoming and asks his son, Japheth, "What kinda tree is so beautiful?" Japheth replies, "It's a flowering peach, Poppa" (203). When Noah comments that it is April, the implication is obviously one of rebirth and fertility; for Noah comments further that the tree is ". . . from the new earth" (203).

The Odets version of the Noah story was not concerned with reproducing the details of the biblical version. Odets used his source merely as a point from which to work. Noah, when he first appears, is rather addled. He has just wakened from a dead sleep in which he has dreamed of the destruction of the world. His wife, on hearing this, blames such a fanciful musing on Noah's tendency to tipple. She tells him, "You had enough to drink," when he puts the jug to his lips. He responds, "You should be satisfied that I drink, otherwise I'd leave you" (180). This uncomplimentary banter is basically good-natured, and no real offense is intended by it. Noah and Esther, having been married for sixty years, understand each other very well.

Noah is deeply concerned that he should have had a dream tantamount to a visit from the Almighty. He is a common man and very old. He is not sure of his ability to persuade his three sons, Ham, Shem, and Japheth, to help him build an Ark. He knows that his own strength is not great and, examining his hands, he says, "See them bones? That ain' hands no more, it's bones! . . . Why did You pick me . . .? Honorable Sir . . . ? For what?" (189). Noah is profoundly and unquestioningly reverent, but he feels that the task which God has set for him is too great for his strength and for his abilities.

When Noah sends his unmarried son, Japheth, to bring Shem to him, he does not dare to have Japheth tell Shem that he must leave his harvest because Noah has had a prophecy; Shem is too practical to inconvenience himself during harvest time in order to gratify his father's whim. So Noah instructs Japheth to tell Shem that ". . . a big building proposition came up! The Customer is very impatient, can't wait. . . . Needs an estimate right away" (181). He knows that with this lure he can bring Shem to him. He still, of course, has doubts regarding his ability to convince Shem that he should leave his harvest to help in the construction of the Ark. Shem is hard-headed. When he hears Noah's story, he is respectful for a time, though doubtful. Finally, Japheth indicates that he believes the story of the dream but that despite this, as a protest against God, he will refuse to go on the Ark if it is built. Shem can restrain himself no longer and snaps at Japheth, "Poppa's in his second childhood an' you're not outta your first!" (184).

Ham is even more doubtful than Shem. He asks Noah how he can possibly gather together all of the animals which God has said to go on the Ark. Noah, who has no answer for his sons, is himself concerned about the problem of gathering the necessary pairs of animals. The family bickers, and tempers become short until the tension is finally broken by the appearance of what looks like a mouse. It frightens the women and is the occasion for a great deal of screaming. However, the mouse turns out to be a gitka and it runs directly into Noah's hands. The family is deeply impressed as Noah announces, "God has sent us a gitka" (184). Then Japheth cries out to the family to look out the window: pairs of animals are advancing down the road and a whirring of wings in the air heralds the arrival of pairs of birds which will accompany Noah and his family on the Ark.

Thus does God come to Noah's aid to convince the others that the dream was authentic and not merely a figment of Noah's imagination. This is the first publicly revealed miracle through which God helps Noah. It represents the first major turning point in the narrative; Noah will have the aid of his sons in the building of the Ark. Noah gives thanks to God, saying, "Oh Lord, our God, the soul is rejoiced in Thee and Thy wonders. Here the family . . . is united to serve You as You asked" (185). Fundamentally, Odets is emphasizing here that the family, which, with the marriage of two sons, has drifted apart, is now being reunited through adversity. The unity of the family tends, more and more, to become a central social issue in the play. The family is presented as the fundamental unit of the human race; one family, according to the Noah legend, lived through an incredible experience so that the human race might continue on the face of the earth.

In reviewing *The Flowering Peach*, Harold Clurman, writing in *Nation*, spoke of Odets' identification of himself with both Noah and Japheth. "Noah," wrote Mr. Clurman, "is the essential, instinctive Odets; Japheth the rational, thinking Odets." Odets, at this point, seemed to be at a spiritual crossroads. Noah was the simple, ever-faithful servant of God; but Japheth, portrayed by Odets as a character suggestive of Job, was at once believing and protesting. Japheth, who believed in the validity of his father's dream long before Ham and Shem did, based his belief upon human reason and observation. He told his brothers, "It hasn't rained since early spring . . . floods are possible, I mean. If Poppa says he had the dream, he had it" (183). Japheth tells Shem that if he decides not to help build the Ark, it will not be because he doesn't think the flood is imminent, but rather because he ". . . might decide to die with the others. . . . Someone, it seems to me, would have to protest such an avenging, destructive God!" (184). Shem, who at this point is unwilling to believe in the truth of his father's dream, shows himself to be much more conventional and much less rational in his acceptance of the prevailing religious faith than is Japheth; he is profoundly shocked, not because Japheth believes in the dream, but because his thinking brother has baldly implied that God might be avenging and destructive.

Japheth is unmarried, and this is a source of great concern to his parents. In an exchange with Noah, during which Noah again prods Japheth to take a wife, Japheth responds, "How can I take a wife in times like these?" Noah tells him that God wants him to take a wife because ". . . the new world will need babies, bushels an' bushels of babies." Japheth, with a characteristically skeptical question, brings the scene to a climax by asking, "And what about the bushels of babies who will die in the flood? . . . is this vengeful God the very God I was taught to love?" And thus saying Japheth announces that he cannot continue to work on the building of the Ark: "I cannot work for this brutal God!" (187). So saying Japheth takes his leave of the family, thereby causing the work on the Ark to come to a standstill. Noah still has his unquestioning faith and can say with genuine conviction that ". . . The Lord is good for anybody an' everybody, at all times!" (188). But he is now in a crucial situation because the time of the flood is fast approaching. An old man who has not the physical strength and vitality to do the sort of work of which Japheth is capable, he bemoans his lack of vigor and goes to his rest that evening with dejection. His sleep is so troubled that Esther becomes alarmed and calls her sons to waken him. Upon doing so, they find that Noah is no longer an old man; he has been miraculously transformed into a strong ". . . young man of fifty, with eagle-bright eyes and reddish hair" (189). God has performed this miracle so that the course of events which He has predetermined shall not be impeded.

So strong are the family ties in the play that Japheth cannot really leave the family, and he returns to help complete the Ark. Life is difficult for the entire family; when Noah goes into town, people cast stones at him; and other members of the family are rebuked by those about them. As the time of the flood approaches, there are signs from heaven to indicate that an unusual event is nigh; these signs are observed only by the members of Noah's family. Shem, once the most dubious of the sons, is struck dumb when he observes these signs, and becomes the son who most firmly believes in the coming of the flood. He says in dismay, "The sun is rising in the west and setting in the east! Why don't people see it? Where are their brains?" (190).

Throughout the action of the play, Shem, the businessman of the family, is portrayed as an opportunist. He accepts his faith largely on opportunistic grounds. He tends to play both ends against the middle in a rather amusing way. For example, because he believes in the inevitability of the flood, he sells all of his land. Obviously, the flood, if it eradicates the lives of all earthly creatures save those in the Ark, will bring about a situation in which the conventional economic system will be meaningless. Nevertheless, Shem hoards the proceeds from the sale of his goods and attempts to evade the payment of taxes on his gain. Similarly, it is Shem and his wife Leah who nearly sink the Ark after it is adrift for many days by hoarding manure. From this manure Shem intends to make ". . . dried manure briquettes," which will be sold after the waters have receded. Noah is appalled by Shem's hoarding and, in a humorous scene, says, "On the Holy Ark he's makin' business! Manure! With manure you want to begin a new world!" (197).

Ham is the playboy among Noah's sons. He is impetuous and, for the most part, forthright. He no longer loves his wife Rachel who feels towards Japheth a deep love which Japheth reciprocates. Ham is in love with Goldie, the young woman who saved Japheth from being beaten by an aroused throng of people and who is the only human outside Noah's immediate family to be taken on the Ark. It is, of course, hoped by Noah that Japheth and Goldie will marry.

Once the family is aboard the Ark, Ham seduces Goldie and then demands further attentions from her, securing her assent by threatening to tell those on board what they already have reason to suspect: that the two are having an affair. Despite this, Ham is portrayed with sympathy and one does not receive the impression that he is despicable. Indeed, the Ark begins to become a place of rather casual moral conduct. Noah tries to resist and suppress this tendency; however, Esther accepts it and deals tactfully with the four who are involved in illicit romances. It is Esther who tries to persuade Noah to permit these four to be married; even as she is on the brink of death, she says to Noah, "Marry the children . . . for the sake of happiness in the world" (201). But Noah is adamant; and, though he finds it very painful to deny his wife's dying wish, he must say to her, "Old friend, it hurts me to refuse you, but it stands in the books for a thousand years." Esther protests that all the books are in the water now and that perhaps Noah does not really know the wishes of God. But Noah assures her that God has concern for them and that He will provide for them a promised land. To this Esther, now much more the rationalist than she has ever been previously, retorts, "The children, their happiness . . . is my last promised land" (202).

In essence, the understanding Esther is denying the intractable God of the Hebrews, the God to whom Noah pays unquestioning homage, and is putting her family first, again emphasizing the extreme social importance of the family. This is Odets writing of any typical Jewish mother. Noah and Esther have, through this scene, become universalized symbols of Man and of Woman. The male upholds the greater laws of the universe; the female upholds the family, the seat of human love and of biological continuance.

Noah serves as a reassuring testament to the endurance of the laws of the Hebrews. He is not a learned man, but he knows and understands the law of his faith. When, in Scene V, three ancient patriarchs appear to ask Noah to take them on the Ark in order that the Old Law be preserved, Noah has to refuse them because God has appointed who is to go. The men point out that they ". . . know the Old Law *behind* the Old Law," but still Noah must carry out God's command. The implication clearly is that the obedient servant gains favor in the eyes of God. It is not necessary that this servant know the Old Laws behind the Old Laws; it is necessary only that he know the will of God and carry it out faithfully and unquestioningly.

Japheth's role in *The Flowering Peach* is a most interesting one. He, among the sons, is the mainstay of the family. His problem is one which involves the principles upon which his life has been based. Japheth, from a rise in the land, looks down upon the landscape below him and says, "Those roads down there! . . . They're not cobwebs, those roads, the work of a foolish spider, to be brushed away by a peevish boy! Those roads were made by man, crazy not to be alone or apart! Men crazy to reach each other! Well, they won't now" (192). But Rachel reminds Japheth that the Ark is the only hope now, and that the only idealism depends upon man's survival. Esther reinforces this point when she tells Japheth that it is hollow to die in protest, that the only real protest is to ". . . have your own sons an' teach them!" (193).

Ultimately, Noah knocks Japheth out and has him carried onto the Ark. Once he regains consciousness, Japheth is insistent that the Ark should have a rudder and should be steered. Noah protests that this was not God's intention; again, reason and faith are sharply in conflict.

The Flowering Peach has been grossly misunderstood. Few people, apparently, were able to see that the story was actually very timely and that Odets' message was pointedly directed at man in the midst of the twentieth century. The play was written during a time of grave international tensions which might easily have erupted into a nuclear war that could have resulted in the sort of mass annihilation brought about by the flood in the Noah story. But Eric Bentley, who wrote enthusiastically about the play in *New Republic*, considered ". . . the drama of ideas . . . a subplot" and viewed the family romance as the main plot. While he called *The Flowering Peach* ". . . the best American play I have ever reviewed in these columns," he felt that the subplot was troublesome.

The play, which ran for one hundred and thirty-five performances on Broadway, received much adverse criticism for its presentation of frequent family squabbles on the Ark. It must be remembered, however, that the members of the family were under immense and constant emotional strain during the entire action of the play and that the confinement on the Ark, which lasted for nearly a year in the Odets version of the story, was condensed by the author to a bare minimum. The bickering was necessary to depict the tensions which existed, and it would hardly have been convincing to present a more harmonious and complacent family.

The Flowering Peach was also criticized by some for lacking the social indignation of the author's early works. This criticism was best countered by John Mason Brown, who pointed out that the play, had it been written by Odets twenty years earlier, ". . . would have quavered with energy, been fired with indignation, and probably ended with all the passengers on the Ark organizing a union." Brown goes on to commend Odets for the compassion, humor, and gentle affirmation of *The Flowering Peach,* and to note the play's significance ". . . in a world once again imperiled."[5]

The play is called ". . . literal and human in conception" by Miss Wyatt, the reviewer for *Catholic World,* who also notes that the freedom with which Odets has handled the biblical version of the Noah story adds charm and warmth to the play. *Time* also spoke favorably of the play's ". . . child-like scrambling of time and place." Robert Whitehead commented in *Theatre Arts* that, ". . . [Odets'] work reflects . . . strikingly certain American national characteristics: rebelliousness [Japheth], virility [Noah], and violence coupled with tenderness, sentiment and humor [also Noah]." *Newsweek* applauded Odets for having mellowed while having ". . . lost none of his feel for words and none of his real sense of theatre."

Among those who felt that *The Flowering Peach* did not represent a step forward for Odets was Maurice Zolotow, who, writing in *Theatre Arts*, stated that Odets seemed to be looking for something in ". . . the mythology of orthodox Judaism," but he did not quite know what it is. As a result, according to Zolotow, ". . . the play is dissolved in murky confusion."

Also among those who felt that the play did not meet expectations was Gerald Weales, who, in *Commentary*, objected to the dullness of the play and to the fact that Odets' Noah did not have ". . . a more valid relation to his surroundings." He felt that the play lacked the vigorous language of *Awake and Sing!* and that Odets, writing as an American Jew, lost much of the humor of the European Jew. Wolcott Gibbs, in *The New Yorker*, objected that ". . . the humor not only is generally out of key with lofty pathos but often . . . has the embarrassing effect of presenting the Almighty as an accessory clown." Weales also stated that "any new tradition would have to lie where Odets, in his early plays, vaguely sees it, in the communities with a Jewish population dense enough to allow its members to retain a group personality even while they absorb everything that is more widely American." Weales did not think that Odets sufficiently established the background of the folk play to have *The Flowering Peach* present a convincing degree of dramatic validity.

A reading of *The Flowering Peach* is vital to anyone who would view Odets as a mature and well-developed artist rather than as a radical playwright who wishes to use the stage as a soapbox. Unfortunately this most significant Odets play has not been published in its entirety, so is not easily available to the public. It is to be hoped that this most unfortunate omission will one day be remedied.

IV *The Third Major Period*

The third major period in Odets' creative life, represented by the three dramas written between 1949 and 1954, has been fruitful indeed, for it has marked the most varied period in his writing. He has, during this time, turned his attention to social problems with which, in the 1930's, he would not have been conversant. However, Odets has not grown in popularity. He has suffered from the sort of criticism which bemoaned the passing of the angry Odets of the depression years.

It is exceedingly difficult for anyone familiar with the Odets of *Waiting for Lefty* and *Golden Boy* to judge his later works strictly on their own merits. It must be remembered that the fiery Odets who, in 1935, had seen three of his plays received by New York audiences with unrestrained enthusiasm, had come of age at a time when the social and economic issues brought about by the Great Depression were in the forefront of most minds. He wrote with force and with deep personal feeling of these issues and his writing met an immediate social need. His writing during this period was irresistibly forceful although it was not always artistically exemplary. Odets was so completely caught up in the social issues of the 1930's that he was not concerned with the artistry of his productions.

It was only as the pressing issues of the 1930's had become less pressing and had drawn nearer to solution that Odets was able to enter a phase of artistic experimentation which, in the lives of many artists, occurs much earlier. *Waiting for Lefty* was written in three days of impassioned and feverish activity; *The Country Girl* passed through three distinct versions before anyone was permitted to read it. *Till the Day I Die* was written as a *tour de force* in a matter of days and was presented almost immediately; *Clash by Night* was rewritten nine times before its final presentation. Obviously, the Odets of the 1940's and 1950's was grappling with new techniques and with new social problems. His underlying concerns are often the same in the later plays as they were in the early ones, but the timeliness of the later plays is not always immediately apparent.

With the beginning of World War II, the issues of the Depression era became history. Many people apparently expected Odets to continue writing about them as though they were still vital; but the author turned to more generalized social issues. The later plays mark a redirection of the author's interests, but not a retrogression in his ability as a playwright. They stand as evidence of his versatility, of his artistic concern, and of his ability to write with restraint of the same issues which he once mounted a soapbox to proclaim abroad.

CHAPTER 6

General Conclusions

FROM THE FOREGOING chapters, it would seem valid to draw certain general conclusions about the course which Clifford Odets' creative activity has followed. In some matters he has been notably consistent throughout his creative life; in other matters he has departed from his original stand.

Through all of the plays considered in this study, it is obvious that the author has had a deep concern with the basic falseness of society and with the effects of this falseness upon human existence. The false standards of capitalism were explored in the earlier plays and were stated for the most part from the viewpoint of the workers and their families. In *The Big Knife*, Charlie Castle is a worker, albeit a very prosperous one; he is still the victim of the capitalistic enterprise, the film industry. He must work constantly to reinforce the false standards of existence which his fans insist upon. Similarly, in *Awake and Sing!*, Bessie Berger always struggles to keep her family within the confines of middle-class morality which is her chief concern.

In all of Odets' plays, the family is of the utmost importance. In most of his plays it is set forth as the basic and most important social institution. This sentiment is just as strong in *The Flowering Peach* as it was in *Awake and Sing!* and in *Paradise Lost*. Even in *Till the Day I Die* the relationship of Ernst Tausig to his brother is fundamental to the ideological development of the play, and while the emphasis on family life is not conventional, it is certainly present.

Odets has constantly asserted in his plays the idea that society cannot function adequately unless all men have the opportunity to gain financial independence in a way which does not force them to make a compromise with their ideals. Odets' social philosophy does not suggest that financial security alone is the solution to man's problems. Ben Stark had a degree of financial security, and he was not at all happy. Charlie Castle had a great degree of financial security and was utterly miserable.

It is important to note that Odets' social concern in the 1930's was timely and topical. In his plays after this period, his basic social concerns did not alter; however, he gave evidence of his artistic versatility by broadening his scope and dealing with situations relating to levels of society with which, in the 1930's, he was but meagerly acquainted. Because Odets has always written about issues and characters which he fully understands, his work has had about it a high degree of authenticity.

Odets has never lost interest in the lower and middle classes of society. It is because America's social scene has changed that this more recent writing has been about issues which are not uniquely lower- or middle-class. As the old problems became dated, he had no choice but to write of issues which were more timely.

Hollywood, contrary to much general opinion, appears not to have ruined Odets as a creative artist. Movie writing, if anything, has made him more adroit and polished in his writing than he was at the beginning of his career. His characterization in the later plays is most convincing and the characters are developed with great verbal economy. In the earlier plays one often comes to know the characters by being told about them; in the later plays, they are developed primarily through their actions, and the development is often swift and direct.

In his early plays, Clifford Odets suggested answers to the ills of a troubled society. There is often a call to action of some sort in the early plays, and the action suggested is usually affirmative in nature. However, in *Golden Boy, Rocket to the Moon, Clash by Night,* and *Night Music* there are strong overtones of negation, suggesting that Odets is struggling with himself, trying to find answers but unable to do so. *The Country Girl* and *The Big Knife* do not contain the affirmation of the early plays and it is obvious that in these plays Odets is still engaged in an ideological struggle on a scale much broader than the mere subject matter of his dramas. Only in *The*

Flowering Peach does there appear to be a real mellowing in the author. This play is richly affirmative and, to a large degree, is similar to the social conflicts which Odets has witnessed. The play depicts the inevitability of human struggle and the necessity of acceptance of that which cannot be forestalled. But the play ends with the thought that continuance is inescapable. The earth has been almost totally depopulated; but a few have been saved and they will repopulate the earth. Life will go on despite the rigors of human existence.

It is perhaps too early to indicate Odets' position in the history of American drama. It seems evident that he is not of the stature of Eugene O'Neill; however, he may well be called the most significant of the specifically proletarian playwrights of the 1930's. His poetic use of language, his accurate capturing and reproduction of the vernacular, as well as his keen understanding of human motivation, have led the way to such modern playwrights as Arthur Miller, Tennessee Williams, and Truman Capote. It would not seem extravagant to state that the name Clifford Odets is firmly fixed and importantly placed in the drama of twentieth-century America.

Notes and References

Chapter One

1. Harold Clurman, *The Fervent Years*, p. 35.
2. The emphasis was on the actor's attaining truth on the stage, in accordance with the Stanislavsky method. Great emphasis was placed upon improvisation, and actors were required to speak *ad libitum* very often. They were also required to engage in exercises in "affective memory," a Stanislavsky device, which required the actor to produce a given mood by recalling the details of an actual event in his own past which evoked such a mood from him. For details of this, see Clurman, *op. cit.*, pp. 42-44.
3. *Loc. cit.*, XXXII (December 5, 1938), 46.
4. Clurman, *op. cit.*, pp. 67-68.
5. Joseph Wood Krutch, *American Drama Since 1918: An Informal History*, pp. 263-64.
6. John D. Hart, ed., *The Oxford Companion to American Literature*, 3rd. ed., p. 544.
7. *Wilson Library Bulletin*, XI (February, 1937), 374.
8. This fragmentary play was entitled *The Law of Flight* and was written by Odets in 1937. See Clurman, *op. cit.*, pp. 219-20.
9. For a discussion of the development of this theme in the 1920's see J. Aldrich, *After the Lost Generation*, Chapter II.

Chapter Two

1. See Peter Lisca, "*The Grapes of Wrath* as Fiction," *PMLA*, LXXII (1957), 296-309.
2. *Six Plays of Clifford Odets*, p. 429.

Chapter Three

1. Letter from Clifford Odets to Marian Gallaway dated New York, June, 1940, and cited in Gallaway's unpublished doctoral dissertation *A Comparative Study of the Development of Skills in Plot Construction by a Group of Living American Dramatists*, p. 8.
2. John Howard Lawson, *Theory and Technique of Playwrighting*, p. 253.

3. Page notations throughout this chapter refer to the Modern Library Edition of *Six Plays of Clifford Odets*.

4. This scene is reproduced in *Proletarian Literature in the United States*, ed. Granville Hicks, pp. 289-93. It is also included in the first published version of the play in *New Theatre and Film*, II (February, 1935), 13-20.

5. For a discussion of the problem of a declining birth rate, see A. M. Schlesinger, *The Rise of Modern America*, p. 376. Schlesinger notes that the birth rate, which had jumped one-quarter to one-third in every decade down to 1890, had declined to sixteen per cent in the decade beginning in 1920, and during the next decade had declined to seven per cent. Statisticians were predicting that the population of the United States would cease expanding by the end of the century.

6. See Winifred L. Dusenbury, *The Theme of Loneliness in Modern American Drama*.

7. Lawson, *op. cit.*, pp. 252-53.

8. Albert Hunt, "Only Soft-Centered Left: Odets and Social Theatre," *Encore*, VIII (May-June, 1961), 6.

9. Anita Block, *The Changing World in Plays and Theatre*, p. 288.

10. Hunt, *op. cit.*, p. 10.

11. Block, *op. cit.*, pp. 286-87.

12. Harold Clurman as quoted in *Six Plays of Clifford Odets*, p. 423.

13. Joseph Mersand, *The American Drama, 1930-1940: Essays on Playwrights and Plays*, p. 84.

14. Eleanor Flexner, *American Playwrights: 1918-1938*, p. 298.

Chapter Four

1. Rosamund Gilder, *Theatre Arts Monthly*, XXIII (January, 1939), 15.

2. *Time*, LXXVIII (November 17, 1961), 34.

3. *American Drama Since 1918: An Informal History*, p. 274.

4. Harold Clurman, *The Fervent Years*, pp. 261-62.

5. Stark Young as quoted by Joseph Mersand, *The American Drama, 1930-1940: Essays on Playwrights and Plays*, p. 73.

6. *Loc. cit.*, p. 279.

7. *Commonweal*, XXV (January 16, 1942), 319-20.

Chapter Five

1. A. Aulicino, "How the *Country Girl* Came about, in the Words of the People Involved," *Theatre Arts*, XXXVI (May, 1952), 57.

Notes and References

2. *New Republic*, CXXIII (December 11, 1950), 29-30.
3. Aulicino, *op. cit.*, p. 55.
4. "The First 15 Years," *New Republic*, CXXIII (December 11, 1950), 29.
5. "On the Crest of the Waves," *Saturday Review*, XXXVIII (January 15, 1955), 30.

Selected Bibliography

PRIMARY SOURCES

Awake and Sing! New York: Covici-Friede, 1935.

The Big Knife. New York: Random House, 1949.

Clash by Night. New York: Random House, 1942.

The Country Girl. New York: Dramatists' Play Service, Inc., 1949. Acting Edition.

The Flowering Peach. New York: Dramatists' Play Service, Inc., 1954. This play is available presently only in typescript. An abridged version appears in *The Best Plays of 1954-55*, edited by Burns Mantle and Louis Kronenberger, New York: Dodd, Mead and Company, 1955.

Golden Boy. New York: Random House, 1937.

"I Can't Sleep: A Monologue." *New Theatre and Film*, III (February, 1936), 8-9.

Night Music. New York: Random House, 1940.

Paradise Lost. New York: Random House, 1936.

Rocket to the Moon. New York: Random House, 1939.

"Silent Partner." *New Theatre and Film*, IV (March, 1937), 5-9.

Six Plays of Clifford Odets. New York: Random House, 1939. This volume was also issued in the same year in the Modern Library Edition, in which the pagination was identical and the contents are as follows: Preface by Odets; *Waiting for Lefty; Awake and Sing!; Till the Day I Die; Paradise Lost; Golden Boy; Rocket to the Moon;* Introductions by Harold Clurman to *Awake and Sing!, Paradise Lost,* and *Golden Boy.*

Three Plays by Clifford Odets. New York: Covici-Friede, 1935. Contents: *Waiting for Lefty; Awake and Sing!* and *Till the Day I Die.*

"Waiting for Lefty." *New Theatre and Film*, II (February, 1935), 13-20.

Waiting for Lefty and *Till the Day I Die.* New York: Covici-Friede, 1935.

Mr. Odets also collaborated with Carleton Beals on a pamphlet entitled *Rifle Rule in Cuba.* New York, 1935.

SECONDARY SOURCES

A. *Published Works*

To date no full-length studies of Clifford Odets have been published. However, the following published works contain significant materials concerning Odets and his work.

BENTLEY, ERIC. *The Playwright as Thinker.* New York: Harcourt, Brace and Company, 1955. A consideration of the conceptual patterns and trends in Odets' plays; excellent presentation of Odets as a realist.

BLOCK, ANITA. *The Changing World in Plays and Theatre.* Boston: Little, Brown and Company, 1939. A balanced discussion of the social forces which motivated Odets in the writing of his early plays.

CLURMAN, HAROLD. *The Fervent Years: The Story of the Group Theatre and the Thirties.* New York: Alfred A. Knopf, 1945. Presents Odets in relation to the training he received in the Group Theatre; also presents intimate insights by one of his closest friends and most understanding critics.

DUSENBURY, WINIFRED L. *The Theme of Loneliness in Modern American Drama.* Gainesville: University of Florida Press, 1960. Traces the theme of loneliness through Odets' plays up to *Night Music;* a very penetrating appraisal.

FLANAGAN, HALLIE. *Arena.* New York: Duell, Sloan and Pearce, 1940. Traces the effect of Federal Theatre upon the drama and the play-consciousness of the 1930's.

FLEXNER, ELEANOR. *American Playwrights: 1918-1938.* New York: Simon and Schuster, 1938. Provides a comprehensive overview of the dramatic activity of the years in which Odets was doing his most extensive writing.

KRUTCH, JOSEPH WOOD. *American Drama Since 1918: An Informal History.* New York: George Braziller, Inc., 1957. Traces the rise of realism in modern American drama and relates Odets to this movement; presents excellent insights on social drama.

LAWSON, JOHN HOWARD. *Theory and Technique of Playwrighting.* New York: Hill and Wang, 1960. This book provides the best presentation in print of the technical and structural elements of Odets' early plays.

LUMLEY, FREDERICK. *Trends in 20th Century Drama.* Fair Lawn: Essential Books, Inc., 1956. This book has considerable scope, but its judgments tend to be superficial.

MERSAND, JOSEPH. *The American Drama, 1930-1940: Essays on Playwrights and Plays*. New York: The Modern Chapbooks, 1941. One of the earliest lengthy appraisals of Odets and his work; biographical details sometimes obscure critical analysis.

NANNES, CASPER. *Politics in the American Drama as Revealed by Plays Produced on the New York Stage, 1890-1945*. Philadelphia: University of Pennsylvania Press, 1950. Gives special attention to *Till the Day I Die*.

O'HARA, FRANK H. *Today in American Drama*. Chicago: University of Chicago Press, 1939. Chapter Five, which is devoted to social drama, has particular relevance.

B. *Unpublished Studies*

GALLAWAY, MARIAN H. *A Comparative Study of the Development of Skills in Plot Construction by a Group of Living American Dramatists*. Unpublished doctoral dissertation, University of Iowa, 1941. Gives considerable attention to Odets' technique.

PENROD, JOHN A. *American Literature and the Great Depression*. Unpublished doctoral dissertation, University of Pennsylvania, 1954. Considers Odets to be less proletarian in his outlook than most critics have indicated.

WILSON, RICHARD E. *A Director's Production Book for Clifford Odets' The Flowering Peach*. Unpublished master's thesis, Stanford University, 1959. Provides an excellent, comprehensive view of Odets in Chapter One and a valuable interpretation of *The Flowering Peach*.

C. *Articles about Odets*

BROWN, JOHN MASON. "The Man Who Came Back." *Saturday Review of Literature*, XXXIII (December 9, 1950), 26-27. Interesting insights on "the new Odets" as exemplified in *The Country Girl* and *The Big Knife*.

BRUSTEIN, ROBERT. "America's New Culture-Hero: Feeling without Words." *Commentary*, XXV (February, 1958), 123-29. Notes lack of verbal coherence in the proletarian heroes of such modern playwrights as Odets and Williams.

"Clifford Odets." *Wilson Library Quarterly*, XI (February, 1937), 374. A very brief consideration, dealing primarily with biographical details.

CLURMAN, HAROLD. "The First 15 Years." *New Republic*, CXXIII (December 11, 1950), 29-30. Basically a review of *The Country Girl*, though the author views Odets in perspective and comments on his basic poetic ability.

Selected Bibliography

FAGIN, N. B. "In Search of an American *Cherry Orchard.*" *Texas Quarterly,* I (Summer-Autumn, 1958), 132-41. Claimed Odets was influenced by *The Cherry Orchard* only insofar as it lends itself to universal historical analogy.

FERGUSON, OTIS. "Pay-off on Clifford Odets." *New Republic,* C (September 27, and October 4, 1939), 216-17, 242-43. Basically a review of *Six Plays of Clifford Odets;* comments on Odets' understanding of Jewish family life and claims that he "holds a corner on living drama."

GASSNER, JOHN. "The Long Journey of a Talent." *Theatre Arts Monthly,* XXXIII (July, 1949), 26-31. Comments on the fact that eight years in Hollywood did not eviscerate Odets.

HYAMS, BARRY. "Twenty Years on a Tightrope." *Theatre Arts Monthly,* XXXIX (April, 1955), 68-70, 86. Assessment of *The Flowering Peach;* commentary on the continuance of the theme of not having life nullified.

ISAACS, EDITH. "Clifford Odets." *Theatre Arts Monthly,* XXIII (April, 1939), 257-64. Examines Odets' extreme subjectivity; considers his imagination to be bound by his experience. Attributes to him a rare gift for theatrical rhythms.

KRUTCH, JOSEPH WOOD. "Mr. Odets Speaks His Mind." *Nation,* CXL (April 10, 1935), 427-28. Stresses Odets' ability to state socialistic philosophies in terms the workers would understand. Notes extreme realism in his plays.

McCARTEN, JOHN. "Revolution's Number One Boy." *The New Yorker,* XIV (January 22, 1938), 21-27. This article is filled with valuable biographical data regarding Odets. A most valuable early contribution to Odets scholarship.

"White Hope." *Time,* XXXII (December 5, 1938), 44-47. *Time's* cover article on Odets presents a most comprehensive view of him as a man and as a playwright.

Index

Index

on

Zebra

Leopard

Dassie

WHEN HIPPO
WAS HAIRY

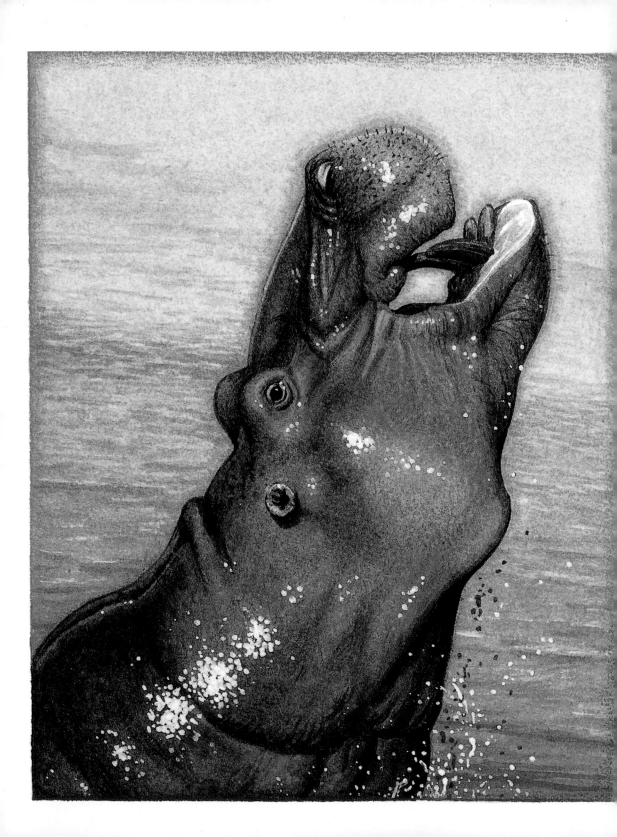

WHEN HIPPO WAS HAIRY

WAS HAIRY

And other tales from AFRICA

Told by Nick Greaves
Illustrated by Rod Clement

New York • Toronto

Dedicated to my father, Roland.

First edition for the United States and Canada
published 1988 by Barron's Educational Series, Inc.

All inquiries should be addressed to:

Barron's Educational Series, Inc.
250 Wireless Boulevard
Hauppauge, New York 11788

Library of Congress Catalog Card No. 88-19273

International Standard Book No. 0-8120-4131-3

Library of Congress Cataloging-in-Publication Data

Greaves, Nick.
When Hippo was hairy and other tales from Africa
told by Nick Greaves; Illustrated by Rod Clement.
144 p. 22 x 17.2 cm.
Summary: A collection of thirty-one stories about
African animals with factual information about each
animal.
ISBN 0-8120-4131-3
1. Animals — Juvenile fiction. 2. Children's stories,
New Zealand. [1. Animals — Fiction. 2. Africa — Fiction.
3. Short stories. 4. Zoology — Africa.]
I. Clement, Rod, ill. II. Title.
PZ 10.3. G798Wh 1988 [Fic] — dc 19 88-19273

A David Bateman Book
Produced by David Bateman Ltd
32-34 View Road
Glenfield, Auckland
New Zealand.

Design — Errol McLeary
Typeset by Typeset Graphics Ltd
Printed in Hong Kong by Everbest Printing Co.

890   987654321

Contents

Acknowledgements

A great many people helped in the preparation of this book — some knowingly, some unwittingly. For their advice and for additional information I am indebted to: Dr. John Hutton, former Curator of Mammology, and Dr. Don Broadley, Curator of Herpetology, both of the Natural History Museum of Zimbabwe; Mr. Ron Thomson, former Provincial Warden, Hwange National Park; Mr. Ian Thomson, former Warden, Matopos National Park; Mr. Ivan Ncube, Provincial Warden, Matabeleland South; Mr. Mike Jones, Terrestrial Ecologist, Hwange National Park, Zimbabwe Department of National Parks and Wildlife Management; Dr. Rosalie Osbourne of the Kenya Wildlife Conservation and Management Department; Mr. Francis Odoom and the Languages Institute of Ghana. Special thanks are also due to Bockie and Rich Peek and Mr. Hadebe, Chief Librarian, the Natural History Museum of Zimbabwe.

A great deal of technical information and support came from Kodak USA and Canon Inc. of Japan. The photographs, I hope, were of assistance to the illustrator, Mr. Rod Clement.

Most of all I am indebted to my wife, Janet; typist, associate editor, rousing supporter and critic, and to my son, Douglas, for being a patient "sounding board."

Introduction

Until quite recently the African continent possessed not only the greatest concentration of wild animals in the world, but the greatest variety too. Sadly, those almost endless herds are now a thing of the past.

The interior of Africa was a place of mystery to all but a handful of adventurous (and often foolhardy) explorers, hunters and missionaries, until the early 1900s. The memoirs of men like Thomas Baines, David Livingstone, P. Courtney Selous and Jonathan Speake, tell us how rich and bountiful was the wildlife of such areas as the East African Plateau and the Karoo.

However, among them, the "gentlemen hunters," the Voortrekkers, the ivory hunters and eventually the farmers, started a slaughter so complete that in many areas of Africa the indigenous animals were exterminated.

Luckily, people have now come to recognize the richness and beauty of the few remaining wilderness areas, and much is being done to conserve them. The benefits of conservation are both financial and aesthetic — but it is future generations who pose the greatest threat to the remaining wildlife.

As Africa's population explodes at an alarming rate, people will require more food and therefore more land, which is a limited resource. Already game parks and sanctuaries are being eyed with envy by land-hungry people. Let us hope that we can develop the future without the destruction that has typified Africa's development in the past.

One of the legacies of Africa's erstwhile teeming wildlife is the wealth of folklore and mythology surrounding it. Indeed, the richness of the lore mirrors the richness of the wildlife. Many of the tales, although told by different tribes from region to region, are basically similar, and they remain a source of knowledge and enjoyment to us and to future generations.

This book attempts to illustrate to our ever-expanding urban population not only the folklore and mythology, but some of the more interesting facts about various animals of the African bush.

The tales of old need not be a thing of the past; the wildlife which inspired them, brought endearingly alive by these simple stories, is a part of Africa's heritage which should not be forgotten.

General Information

DISTRIBUTION (See maps)
The various animals highlighted in this book are all found in southern Africa, though some are also widely spread throughout the rest of sub-Saharan Africa. It is interesting that some species restricted to southern Africa, such as the tsessebe, rock dassie and chacma baboon, do have very close relatives in other parts of the continent. These close relatives, such as the kongoni (an East African hartebeest similar to the tsessebe), the yellow-spotted rock dassie and the yellow baboon, look similar, live in similar habitats and have similar habits, but to the scientist their differences, though often subtle, are sufficient for them to be classified as separate species.

Most species are now confined to areas of sanctuary, such as national parks and ever-diminishing areas of wilderness. Man has to manage these areas carefully to ensure that a healthy environment is maintained for all members of the animal and plant communities. Some large species, such as elephant and buffalo, must at times be culled to prevent their numbers rising above an area's ability to maintain a state of balance. A few species, such as the baboon, jackal and leopard, have been able to take advantage of man's presence, despite ruthless persecution, and are still widely distributed.

Species such as the black rhino have in recent years been drastically reduced in numbers and range because of intense poaching by man. The white rhino, on the other hand, has been brought back from extinction and is a rare success story in African conservation. The last few rhinos were protected in a nature reserve in Zululand and after careful management over the last 60 years have increased in number. The operation has been so successful that white rhinos can now be reintroduced to areas where they once used to roam. Sadly, the northern race of the white rhino was less fortunate and has also been methodically poached to the brink of extinction.

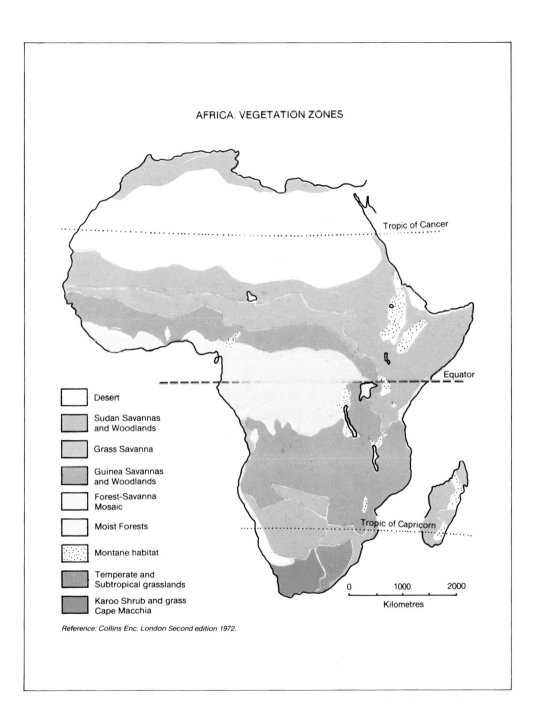

AFRICA. VEGETATION ZONES

Tropic of Cancer

Equator

Tropic of Capricorn

- Desert
- Sudan Savannas and Woodlands
- Grass Savanna
- Guinea Savannas and Woodlands
- Forest-Savanna Mosaic
- Moist Forests
- Montane habitat
- Temperate and Subtropical grasslands
- Karoo Shrub and grass Cape Macchia

0   1000   2000
Kilometres

Reference: Collins Enc. London Second edition 1972.

11

The maps offer a general guide to an animal's distribution. A species may not occur throughout large tracts of its range because of the activities of man, especially if the animal is considered a threat or as competition. To illustrate this, most species occurred down through to the Cape of Good Hope in South Africa when European settlers arrived four centuries ago, but because of hunting and persecution, very few large mammals now exist outside of a few national parks. The same pressure is being exerted on wildlife today in East Africa as the human population grows at alarming speed, displacing the once-teeming populations of plains wildlife.

It is interesting to compare the distribution of the various animals with the vegetation zones of Africa. A lot of information about the animals' habits and diet, etc., can be obtained from this simple exercise.

INFORMATION

The data on size, weight, lifespan, etc., are for an average specimen and, therefore are more representative than quoting Rowland Ward trophy sizes. This information should help one to appreciate differences in sizes and lifestyles of the various animals.

Note: Heights quoted are at the shoulder unless stated otherwise.

AFRICAN TRIBES

Though language, customs and dress can vary dramatically among the native peoples of Africa, a common ancestry can be traced in the folklore, which is remarkably similar throughout much of the continent. Thus, Umvundhla the Hare is the shady character of many a tale in many languages and dialects. It is thought that the tales of Brer Rabbit originated with the slaves transported to the New World from western Africa several centuries ago. This similarity between the tales and subjects is partially explained by the fact that the Bantu peoples of Africa originated from common roots in western central Africa. Over the past 2000 years the Bantu people spread further and further across central, eastern and southern Africa, conquering and assimilating the original inhabitants of these lands.

METRIC CONVERSIONS

For use in countries where the Metric system of measurement is used, the height and weight conversions for the different animals in the Facts sections are:

	Height Male	Height Female	Weight Male	Weight Female	Weight at Birth Male	Weight at Birth Female
Lion	1m	90cm	200kg	130kg	———1.5kg———	
Leopard	75cm	70cm	70kg	60kg	———450g———	
Cheetah	75cm	75cm	60kg	55kg	———300g———	
Wild dog	65cm	65cm	30kg	25kg	———500g———	
Hyena	65cm	70cm	60kg	70kg	———1.5kg———	
Jackal	40cm	38cm	10kg	8kg	———200g———	
Elephant	3m	2.5m	5000kg	3500kg	———120kg———	
White Rhinoceros	1.8m	1.6m	3000kg	2000kg	———40kg———	
Black Rhinoceros	1.4m	1.2m	1500kg	1000kg	40kg	35kg
Hippopotamus	1.5m	1.2m	3000kg	2000kg	———30kg———	
Buffalo	1.6m	1.5m	700kg	600kg	———40kg———	
Baboon	1m	80cm	30kg	18kg	———250g———	
Giraffe	5.5m*	5m*	1200kg	900kg	———100kg———	
Waterbuck	1.3m	1.2m	250kg	200kg	———8kg———	
Zebra	1.2m	1.2m	320kg	280kg	———30kg———	
Tsessebe	1.2m	1.2m	160kg	145kg	———10kg———	
Wart hog	72cm	70cm	70kg	60kg	———800g———	
Hare	15cm	15cm	2.5kg	2kg	———80g———	
Dassie	20cm	20cm	4kg	3kg	250g	200g
Ostrich	2m	1.8m	140kg	120kg	———1.5kg———	
Tortoise	20cm	22cm	1.5kg	2kg	★	

(★ Length at hatching 4cm for both sexes)
(*Full height)

In the Beginning...

The Bushman believes that the Creator made the earth and then the plants upon it. Next, He thought up the many different animals which were to live in the world.

Striking a huge baobab tree, He caused the animals to walk into the light of day for the first time. As each one appeared through a great rent in the tree's roots, He named it and gave it a place to live. Even though He was assisted by Mantis, who was a super-being and the Creator's helper, the animals took a long time to come out of the tree and be named. Last of all came man.

By then, there was only one role left in the great scheme of things, so the Creator and Mantis assigned this place to the Bushman — that of Hunter-Gatherer. The Bushman fulfilled his designated role faithfully, living in close harmony with the animals, birds and the plants upon the earth.

Though the details of this story vary from tribe to tribe, they all record that the animals came before man.

According to Swazi folklore, animals all lived together in peace before the coming of man, and only when he finally appeared, did predation, or meat-eating, spread through the world. Man preyed upon beast; beasts then preyed upon their former friends — even the reptiles and birds copied the deadly example of man. With the coming of man into the world, so fear was born.

Why does the Lion Roar?

(A Batonka story)

After the coming of man into the world, Lion became the most feared of the predators. (As you will remember, the legend said that animals only started to eat meat after man arrived.) In these early days, Lion still had a gentle voice, not very loud at all, and so he was able to catch and eat the other animals without much trouble.

This, of course, greatly worried the other animals, since they never knew when Lion was on the hunt. They decided to hold a meeting to find a way of somehow making Lion less dangerous.

They talked for a long time, but none of them could think of anything. Hare, always the imaginative one, then had a bright idea.

"I know a way that would make Lion's voice like the terrible thunder of a summer's storm," he said, "and then we would always know when he was coming."

The other animals all agreed that this was a marvelous idea. But how was Hare going to manage such a thing? Hare just winked and set off on his difficult task.

Eventually Hare found Lion resting beneath a shady umbrella tree, and approaching him carefully, saying, "O Great One, I am truly most unhappy to bring you bad news, but your brother is very ill, and requests to see you at once." Lion was dreadfully upset to hear this news and told Hare to lead him to his brother as fast as possible.

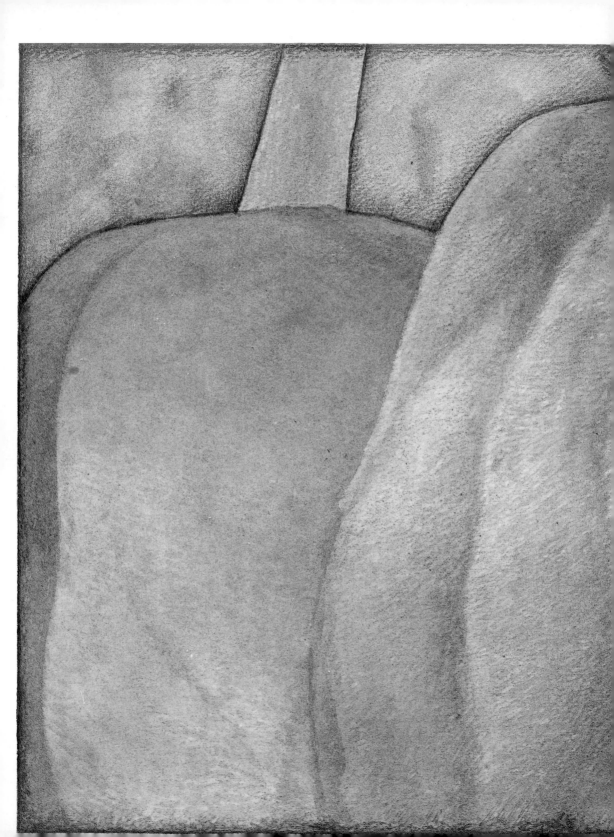

Hare took Lion for miles and miles around the Bushveld and after several hours Lion (who, after all, had been disturbed during his morning sleep) was so weary he could go no further. He lay down in a shady spot and slept.

Now, with the help of a honeyguide bird, the crafty Hare found a wild bees' nest in a tree not too far away. After following the required custom of leaving a good piece of the honeycomb as a "thank-you" for the little bird, Hare took some of the honey and dribbled it all over the paws and head of the sleeping lion. Hare then ran off to some thick bushes nearby and hid.

When the bees returned home and saw that someone had raided their hive, they were terribly angry. They soon found Lion sleeping nearby, with honey all over his paws. In a raging swarm, the bees attacked him, and Lion was stung so many times and was in such pain that his soft cries soon swelled to a thunderous roar that could be heard for miles around!

That is the story of how Lion's voice was changed forever. The animals were very grateful to Hare because, from then on, they could hear Lion's roar from a long way away, and be warned that the King of Beasts was on the hunt.

Why the Lion does not eat Fruit

(A Hambakushu story)

The Hambakush tribe of the Okavango region has this story that explains why Lion does not eat fruit (unless he is driven to it by extreme thirst).

Mbwawa, the jackal, one day discovered the delicious fruit of the thaa tree. But as he sat there enjoying his meal, he heard Lion roaring in the distance. He thought to himself, "Lion sounds hungry. I hope he doesn't come this way and find all my lovely fruit." And he began to worry, since Lion, as everyone knows, has a huge appetite and, being the King of Beasts, is entitled to steal anyone's meal.

Lion did come near, but crafty Mbwawa had thought up a trick to stop Lion from eating his thaa fruit. As soon as Lion was near enough, Mbwawa began to eat the fruit as fast as he could, making sure Lion was watching this display of greed. Suddenly, Mbwawa collapsed in a heap on the ground, writhing and groaning, and then he lay still as if dead. Lion, of course, thought that the fruit must be poisonous, so he went on his way, and soon was out of sight.

Now Mbwawa, getting up, remembered where he had seen the skeleton of another jackal lying nearby. So he fetched it and placed it under the thaa tree on the spot where he had pretended to die. Well satisfied with his clever trick, he went home.

A few weeks later, Lion passed by and saw the thaa tree, laden with juicy-looking fruit. He walked over to the tree, but stopped when he saw the pitiful remains of a jackal. Its bones had been scattered by scavengers, and Lion then remembered seeing Mbwawa eating the fruit. He vowed to himself never to touch fruit again.

Since that day, Lion has never eaten the fruit of the thaa tree, or indeed of any other tree. This made the jackal, and all the other small animals of the bush, very happy. Now they could eat as much fruit as they wanted without having to share it with the lion's enormous appetite.

FACTS ABOUT LIONS
SPECIES:
LION *(Pantheia leo)*
Males often solitary.
Females live in family groups called prides with up to 12 adults.

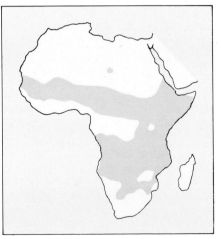

	Male	Female
Height	3⅓ ft	3 ft
Weight	440 lb	290 lb
Weight at Birth	3⅓ lb	3⅓ lb
Age at Weaning	8 months	8 months
Age at Maturity	4 years	3 years
Gestation Period	—	3½ months
Number of Young	—	2-5
Lifespan	20 years	20 years

Habitat All types of country except forest and mountain.
Habits Lions hunt singly, in pairs and in family parties. When harried they tend to become nocturnal, though normally they move and hunt during the cooler parts of the day, lying in shade during the heat between the hours of 10 a.m. and 4 p.m. Prides will combine to hunt, the males normally driving the prey

on to females waiting under cover where their remarkable powers of hiding enable them to blend with the background.

Unmolested they are seldom dangerous, particularly by day. However, they are always potentially aggressive because, being highly intelligent, they are also nervous, high strung and their moods can change with amazing speed.

Lions are the only kind of cat that live in groups (called prides). A pride is made up of females and their young, the cubs, and one fully-grown male lion, the pride leader.

The female lions stay with the pride all their lives, but not so the male lions; only the biggest and strongest one rules the pride. He is always suspicious of the young male lions who are growing up, in case they become stronger than he is, and he always drives them away from the pride before they are too big. This may seem cruel, but it is nature's way of making sure that the only lions to have cubs are the biggest, strongest ones, so that the cubs grow up big and strong too, and become good hunters in their turn.

When the young male lions are driven away, they either live alone or in small groups of "bachelor" lions. There they learn the ways of the bush, and how to kill for themselves. The best and strongest of them may be able to establish a pride of his own.

Lions normally drink every night, but when no rain falls for a long time they are surprisingly hardy. They go for days without water, but like every other animal in times of drought, they look out for juicy tsama melons and gemsbok cucumbers to keep them going.

Diet Lions are carnivorous, normally preying on buffalo, larger antelopes, zebra, ostriches, wild pigs, and occasionally giraffes and baby elephants. When desperately hungry, nothing is too small, and even man may provide a meal, though man-eating is comparatively rare. They will also raid stock when their normal food is scarce.

Breeding Breeding occurs throughout the year. The cubs, usually two to four in a litter, are born in thickets and other sheltered places. When they are very young the lioness remains with them while the male brings her food, or a group of lionesses will sometimes share looking after the cubs.

Lions are polygamous. Several lionesses may associate with one male and bear his cubs. Occasionally, two males may share one lioness but usually the more powerful drives the other away.

The Dreadful Crime of Kadima the Hare

(A Hambakushu story)

Once upon a time, say the Hambakush people, Kadima the hare had an agreement with Nthoo, the leopardess. In exchange for guarding the leopardess' three cubs while she was away hunting, Kadima was given a share of the kill for his supper.

This convenient arrangement worked very well until a hard drought came to the land. The wild animals which Nthoo hunted, all moved away to find water in other regions, and times became very hard for the leopardess, her cubs and Kadima. Day after day, Nthoo came home with nothing for them to eat, and soon they were starving.

Then, one day, Nthoo came home to find that Kadima was eating, and when questioned as to how he had come by the food when she, the finest hunter in the land, had failed to find anything, Kadima replied that a little duiker had wandered past the cave. He had managed to catch and kill it. But the truth was, that the meat that Kadima was eating was really one of the leopardess' cubs!

The next day Nthoo hunted again, and the wicked Kadima killed another of her cubs and ate it. When the leopardess returned empty-handed again that evening, she lay down wearily and asked Kadima to bring her cubs, so that they could be nursed. The crafty Kadima carried the one remaining cub to Nthoo three times, and so tricked her into believing all her cubs were alive and well.

The next morning, after Nthoo had departed, Kadima was so tempted by his hunger that he killed and ate the last leopard cub. To cover his crime he laid false trails to and from the cave, scratching up the undergrowth and breaking branches to make it look as though there had been a great fight.

Then he went down to the dried-up waterhole and painted himself bright red with ochre. When Nthoo returned home, he staggered towards her, weeping, and told her that her cubs had been killed by men who had carried them off to be eaten. He had tried to defend them, he said, but the hunters had beaten him off and he had almost bled to death from his wounds. And he pointed to the red stains on his fur.

Poor Nthoo! Her roar of grief and rage shook the heavens. In a terrible fury, she set off toward the nearest kraal, determined to take her revenge upon the people who had killed her children.

However, just as the leopardess was about to spring upon a group of young herd boys from the village, a loud voice cried out from the tree tops, "Nthoo!" It was the spy of the Bushveld, the Go-way bird. "Nthoo!" he screamed again. "Kadima was the wicked one who killed your children, not the good people of the village!"

Nthoo turned back in rage to seek out Kadima, but Kadima had heard the bird, and fled in terror.

Nthoo the leopardess never caught Kadima the hare, but it is said by the Hambakush people that she searches still.

That is why the leopardess is wary and now always hunts alone; and that is why the hare runs for its life without even looking back, if you should come upon it unawares.

Why the Leopard Hides his Food up a Tree

(A Ndebele story)

The Ndebele tell their children that long ago, there were three friends: the beautiful leopard, the jackal and the hyena. They went everywhere together. Whenever Leopard killed an animal, he would always leave part of it for his friends so that they could have a good feed too.

One day it happened that Leopard was ill, and so he could not hunt. "Jackal," he said, "Please catch some food for us, for I am not well."

But lazy Jackal said, "No. I am too weary. Ask Hyena."

So Leopard said, "Hyena, please hunt for us today, for I am not well enough to do so."

But Hyena, too, made an excuse: "No, I have a sore foot."

At this Leopard roared in anger. "I thought you were my friends, but you are a no-good, lazy pair. Never again will I leave you meat when I make my kill. From this day on, I will make sure of it. I shall take what is left and hang it in a tree, when I have eaten all I want. Then neither of you will be able to get at it."

Leopard was true to his word — for since that day he has never left any meat for his selfish friends. Up into a tree it goes, high out of reach of jackals and hyenas. They have become scavengers now instead, and they eat the scraps that other animals leave behind. It was a sad day for them when they lost Leopard's friendship.

FACTS ABOUT LEOPARDS
SPECIES:
LEOPARD *(Panthera pardus)*
Solitary.

	Male	Female
Height	30 in	28 in
Weight	154 lb	132 lb
Weight at Birth	1 lb	1 lb
Age at Weaning	3 months	3 months
Age at Maturity	2 years	2 years
Gestation Period	—	3 months
Number of Young	—	2 or 3
Lifespan	15 years	15 years

Identification Leopards need not be confused with cheetahs because they are heavier, much more thick-set creatures with shorter legs and a look of great power. Their spots are different too, over most of the body occurring in clusters resembling a rosette whereas the cheetah's are quite separate.

Leopards' coats are a rich, dark sandy-yellow on top graduating to pure white at the throat, inside of the legs and underside of the body. The spots are black.

In high mountain areas leopards occasionally are black all over.

Habitat Leopards live in a wide variety of terrain, from high mountains and rocky country to forest and grasslands and even semi-desert.

Habits Being nocturnal, very wary and elusive, leopards are not often seen. They tend to be solitary and hunt alone although male and female move around together during the mating season.

Leopards often hide up trees during the day, or among rocks, in thick bush, in caves and even in wart hog holes!

When hunting they often lie silently on a tree branch above a game trail and then drop, claws extended, on to the back of the unsuspecting victim. These claws can be fully retracted into the paws, as with all true cats.

Diet Leopards' main prey are impala, but they have a remarkably varied diet which includes insects, fishes, frogs, birds, hyenas, dogs and baboons, which they seem to regard as a particular delicacy.

Breeding There is no particular breeding season. Up to six cubs may be born but the norm is two or three.

How Cheetah got his Speed

(A Bushman story)

Once upon a time the Creator decided to find out which of His animals could run the fastest — and so He entered the cheetah in a race with the tsessebe, which is the swiftest of all the antelopes. The cheetah had soft paws then, and he realized that they were not suited for real speed. So he borrowed a set of paws from an obliging wild dog.

The race started from a high baobab tree. The Creator Himself was in charge, and the two contestants were told to run right across the plains to a hill on the far side. The animals lined up, and then — go! They leapt away.

The tsessebe soon took the lead, and by half-way, he was so far ahead he seemed sure to win. But suddenly — disaster! Tsessebe stumbled on a stone and crashed to the ground; he had broken his leg.

The good-natured cheetah, instead of running past and winning the race, stopped to help his opponent.

The Creator, seeing this, was so pleased by the cheetah's unselfish act that He bestowed upon the cheetah a gift; He made him the fastest animal in the land; and what's more, allowed him to keep the paws of the wild dog.

Why the Cheeks of the Cheetah are Stained with Tears

(A Zulu story)

Long ago, a wicked and lazy hunter was sitting under a tree, gazing idly at a large clearing below where a herd of fat springbok were peacefully grazing. The hunter was thinking that it was far too hot to bother himself with a long and tiring stalk through the bushes, when suddenly he noticed a movement off to the right. It was a female cheetah which had also chosen this herd to hunt — and she was doing it very well.

Keeping downwind of the herd, she was moving closer to them very slowly, inch by inch, and keeping well under cover. The hunter watched, fascinated, as she crept closer and closer to a springbok which had unwisely wandered away from the main herd.

Suddenly, she gathered her long legs under her, and sprang forward like an arrow. With dazzling speed she raced down upon the springbok and caught it just as it started to leap away.

Panting from her effort, the cheetah dragged her prize away to some shade on the edge of the clearing. The hunter watched, marveling at the speed

and skill he had just witnessed. But as he watched, he saw to his surprise that three beautiful cheetah cubs had also been watching and waiting in the shade.

Now the hunter was filled with envy for the cubs, and wished that he, too, could have such a good hunter to provide for him. This gave him a wicked idea; he knew that cheetahs never attack men, and so he decided that it would be easy to take one of the cubs and train it to hunt for him. Chuckling to himself, he settled down to wait. (After all, he was cowardly too, and did not wish to find out whether a mother cheetah would defend her cubs.)

When the sun was setting, the mother cheetah left her cubs concealed in a bush, and set off to the waterhole to drink. Quickly, the hunter grabbed his spear and trotted down to the bushes where the cubs were hidden. There he found the three cubs, still too young to run away. He could not decide which one to take, and so he stole them all, thinking to himself that three cheetahs would undoubtedly be better than one.

When their mother came back half an hour later and found her babies gone, she was broken-hearted. The poor mother cheetah cried and cried, until her tears made dark stains down her cheeks. She wept all night, and all the next day. She cried so loudly that she was heard by an old man, who came to see what all the noise was about.

Now, it so happened that this old man was very wise in the ways of the world, and he had a great knowledge of, and respect for, animals. When he found out what had happened, he became very angry, for not only had the lazy hunter become a thief, but he had broken the traditions of the tribe. All knew that a hunter must use only his own strength and skill. Any other way of hunting was surely a dishonor.

The old man returned to the village and told the other elders what had happened. The villagers became angry, too, and the people found the lazy hunter and drove him away from the village for ever.

The old man took the three cheetah cubs and returned them to their grateful mother; but the long weeping of the mother cheetah had stained her face permanently, and so, to this day, say the Zulu, the cheetah wears the tearstains on its face as a reminder to the hunters that it is not honorable to hunt in any other way than that which is traditional.

FACTS ABOUT CHEETAHS
SPECIES:
CHEETAH *(Acinonyx jubatus)*
Solitary.
ENDANGERED SPECIES

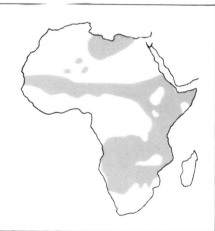

	Male	Female
Height	30 in	30 in
Weight	132 lb	121 lb
Weight at Birth	10 oz	10 oz
Age at Weaning	3 months	3 months
Age at Maturity	2 years	2 years
Gestation Period	—	3 months
Number of Young	—	2-4
Lifespan	10 years	10 years

Identification The cheetah has a lighter body and much longer legs than the leopard, though its overall length is similar. Its spots are different, occurring as individual solid black spots rather than the clusters that characterize the leopard's coat. The cheetah is built for high speed over short distances and even *looks* like a sprinter.

The coat is a similar color to that of the leopard; from dark sandy-yellow on top to pure white under the body and inside the legs. The single black spots occur all over the head, body and legs, blending into bands around the tip of the tail.

Habitat Cheetahs usually live in open country and are very rarely, if ever, found in thick forest.

Habits Widely believed to be the fastest animal on earth, the cheetah has a top speed of around 62 miles per hour (100 km per hour). Its dog-like claws, which do not fully retract like those of a true cat, assist it to reach these speeds by improving grip — like spiked running shoes. These high speeds can only be maintained for relatively short distances — no more than 360 feet. It uses its speed to catch quarry after a short sprint, having first crept up silently. But once winded, the cheetah must give up the chase and look for some other animal.

Having grabbed their prey by the throat, knocked it down and killed it, cheetahs bolt down large quantities of meat very quickly, probably to avoid having it stolen by other predators. Cheetahs will not defend their food and this timid characteristic makes them good-natured pets. When contented they purr like domestic cats!

They are generally solitary and families separate quickly once the cubs have matured.

Diet Medium-sized buck, such as impala, are the cheetah's usual food, though wart hog, guinea-fowl, hares and even ostriches are also taken.

Breeding Two or three cubs are usually born. They are especially beautiful, with long, silver-gray fur. The mother calls to them in a very un-catlike way — with a high-pitched whistle like a bird.

The Revenge of Wild Dog

(A Ndebele story)

Long ago, Wild Dog was very happy, as he possessed a lovely den, a good wife and many children.

Wild Dog was much respected by the animals of the bush, so that when his wife fell ill one day, his cousin Jackal was most concerned. Jackal took Wild Dog to see Hare, for Hare knew the remedies for most ailments.

Hare threw the bones and said that Wild Dog's wife was seriously ill and would get worse. He had a medicine that would make her better, but they could not touch it. They were told to return to the sick wife and tend to her comfort. Hare would see to it that the muti (medicine) would get to them.

Hare then spent all morning preparing the medicine and when he had finished, he called Duiker and told him to carry the medicine in a calabash to the den of Wild Dog. Hare warned Duiker that on no account was he to look back, as that would make the muti useless.

Duiker set off, but on his way he heard trees being broken behind him and, without thinking, he turned around to look. The medicine spilled onto the ground.

Hare was very disappointed to hear Duiker's story, but he prepared some more medicine, and this time he sent Impala on the errand. Impala was given the same warning, but halfway there he was startled by the scent of a lion, looked behind him, and — crash! The calabash fell to the ground and was smashed.

Now, for the third time Hare made up the muti, and this time Zebra volunteered for the task as he felt he was strong and steady enough to handle it.

So Zebra set off, determined to succeed where the smaller animals had failed. He trotted steadily along, and twice along the way heard frightening noises behind him. But he remembered the warning, and ignored them bravely.

Zebra had nearly reached the den of Wild Dog, when suddenly between his front hooves a deadly black mamba reared up, hissing. Zebra jumped and kicked out, terrified of being bitten. Before he could remember Hare's warning, he panicked, turned, and ran for home. As he did so, the calabash fell to the ground and broke into many pieces. Just as this happened, Zebra heard cries and wails of grief coming from Wild Dog's den. The sick wife had waited too long for the medicine and had finally died.

Wild Dog was so distraught with sorrow that he called his family and friends together in a large pack, and together they chased Zebra for many miles. When they caught him they tore him to pieces.

Ever since that time, wild dogs have hunted together in packs. The zebra and impala have always been their special prey, for they have never forgotten the story of the precious medicine that would have saved Wild Dog's beloved wife.

FACTS ABOUT WILD DOGS
SPECIES:
WILD DOG *(Lycaon pictus)*
Gregarious, found in large packs of up to 30.
ENDANGERED SPECIES

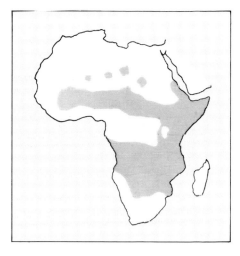

	Male	Female
Height	26 in	26 in
Weight	66 lb	55 lb
Weight at Birth	18 oz	18 oz
Age at Weaning	3 months	3 months
Age at Maturity	12 years	8 years
Gestation Period	—	2 months
Number of Young	—	2-8
Lifespan	10 years	10 years

Identification The large, erect, forward-facing, rounded ears are the most obvious feature of the "Wild," "Hunting" or "Cape Hunting" dog. The dogs are covered in hair which varies greatly in color; no two dogs have the same markings. However, all have a distinctive dark brown or black muzzle and lower face, and a white brush at the tip of the tail.

Habitat The wild dog roams and hunts in open grasslands and light woodlands.

Habits They live in packs of up to 30 and have a well-organized social structure. For example, one or two females will act as "baby-sitters" to several litters of pups while the rest of the pack go hunting.

Old, sick and pregnant members of the pack are also cared for, which is quite unusual as far as the old and sick are concerned in the animal world.

Their hunting technique is also unusually sophisticated. They select a particular animal in the quarry herd, probably one that is sick or disabled. Two or three dogs will then chase it hard, the others loping easily on the flanks or behind. Whenever the "chaser" dogs tire, their place is taken by fresher dogs and this continues until the prey can no longer outrun its hunters.

Diet Wild dogs prey on a wide variety of game, from large animals like zebra down to small antelopes. They sometimes kill livestock and because of this and the way they hunt, man tends to regard them as killers. In reality they perform the important task of culling sick animals before infection can spread.

Breeding A number of pregnant bitches will often give birth together in a special lair, either a deserted anteater hole or other similar shelter.

The Greedy Hyena

(A Shona story)

One fine day, Hyena went out hunting. It was the dry season, so animals were scarce and Hyena was very hungry because he hadn't eaten for several days.

After much searching, Hyena suddenly saw an impala doe and her new fawn. Crouching low, behind a tuft of long grass, Hyena started to think about the fine meal that the young impala would make. He began to drool, and his stomach rumbled quite pleasantly.

"But," he thought, "that mother impala is going to be a bit of a problem." She had no horns, of course, being a female impala, but still she could surely put up quite a fight with her sharp hooves. Hyena decided that if he could kill the mother first, the tender young fawn would then be an easy catch.

So Hyena jumped out from his hiding place and charged straight at the mother impala. She sped off at a fair pace, leading her attacker away from her baby, which ran away in another direction.

After several miles, with the mother impala keeping just out of reach, Hyena realized that she was simply leading him a chase which he could never hope to win. He would never catch the swift impala, and as she disappeared over yet another ridge, he gave up the chase.

"Aha," he thought to himself, "the little fawn is all alone now, and if I hurry back, I'll have my supper before the sun goes down."

Hyena loped back to the starting point, confident that he could easily take the baby impala. But on reaching the place where the chase had

started, Hyena was dismayed to find that the fawn was nowhere to be seen — it had gone back to the safety of the herd, under the watchful eye of its father, the magnificent herd ram. The baby was now waiting for its mother to return from her little jaunt.

Hyena searched about for a long while, but he finally realized that he had foolishly tried to do something that was too difficult for him. If he hadn't been so greedy, trying to catch both the mother and her fawn, he would not have gone to bed hungry that night.

FACTS ABOUT HYENAS
SPECIES:
SPOTTED HYENA (*Crocuta crocuta*)

Gregarious, living in groups of up to 12, called clans.

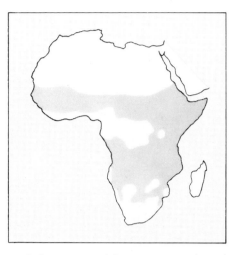

	Male	Female
Height	26 in	28 in
Weight	132 lb	154 lb
Weight at Birth	3⅓ lb	3⅓ lb
Age at Weaning	12 months	12 months
Age at Maturity	2 years	2 years
Gestation Period	—	3 months
Number of Young	—	2-4
Lifespan	20 years	20 years

Identification The most prominent features of the spotted hyena are a large head in proportion to its body, large rounded ears, a sloping back and a short, bushy tail held erect. Its short, coarse coat is a reddish to grayish color with irregular dark spots.

Habitat Hyenas are found in almost every type of country from desert fringes to the snowline.

Habits Because of their gruesome habits and unnerving cries they figure in many African tribes' superstitious beliefs. In fact they are very clever animals with excellent sight, smell and hearing. They will watch for vultures in the sky circling over a kill and use them as guides. They will also wait for hours at a lion's kill until the lion has finished eating.

They generally roam singly or in pairs and don't seem to have any organized social system like the wild dogs.

Diet They are predominantly scavengers, cleaning up the remains of kills left by other animals and thereby performing a very important ecological function. They have immensely powerful jaws and very strong teeth, and so can easily crunch up massive thigh bones and skulls and devour hides. However, they also hunt their own food.

Breeding At mating, large parties of hyenas assemble and make the most terrible racket, often in moonlight.

Up to four pups are born, usually in old anteater holes or similar, sheltered places. After about 6 weeks the pups begin to wander short distances independently and then after a few more weeks go off on their own.

The Tree-climbing Jackal

(A story from Swaziland)

Jackal was well-known for playing tricks on his fellow creatures, so they mistrusted him; but in spite of this, he fooled them time and again. The animals also disliked Jackal because he was a most annoying boaster.

Now one day, while out hunting for food, Jackal met Wildcat, who was lounging elegantly on the branch of a tree. Jackal was jealous, as this was something he could not do.

"Why do you climb trees, Wildcat?" he asked.

Wildcat replied that it gave her an excellent view, so that she could see friend or foe coming from a long way off. Also, climbing trees was a handy way of escaping from the dogs which were forever chasing her.

"Oh, what a coward you are, Wildcat!" sneered the jackal. "Only cowards, snakes and silly birds hide in trees."

Wildcat's feelings were hurt, but she kept her temper, knowing that Jackal was a nasty trickster, and thinking it would be better to keep on the right side of him.

"Do not forget," she replied patiently, "I cannot run as fast as you, and dogs are my natural enemy."

"I can run faster than any creature in the land," boasted Jackal. "Let those scruffy old dogs come — I'm not afraid of them — anyway, I could outrun them any day."

"That may be so," replied Wildcat gently, "but the art of climbing trees has its use in times of trouble, you know. Would you like me to teach you?"

45

Jackal considered this generous offer. "Hmm ... Well, knowledge can never hurt one," he replied airily, "and I've nothing better to do at the moment." Secretly, he was rather anxious to learn.

Wildcat came down from her branch, and Jackal was given his first lesson. But alas, he was not a very good pupil because his claws were too blunt to grip the bark. He kept slipping, and falling on his back in the dirt.

Polite as she was, Wildcat could not help laughing at the sight of Jackal, the oh-so-clever one, scrabbling furiously up the trunk of the tree and falling in a heap every time.

Jackal was getting angrier and angrier, and suddenly he flew into a rage. He turned and snapped at poor Wildcat, grabbing her leg and snarling that he would kill her for making him look ridiculous.

That would most certainly have been the end of Wildcat, but, fortunately for her, a pack of dogs suddenly appeared, barking furiously. Jackal took one look and instantly was no longer the brave animal of his boasting.

He let go of Wildcat's leg and, as she scrambled up her tree to safety, Jackal put his tail between his legs and ran. He dived down a nearby anteater hole just as the dogs were about to catch him. The dogs tried to dig him out, but they could not reach him, so after a while they gave up and went away.

Now Jackal crept out of the hole and, to his shame, saw Wildcat grinning down at him from her perch. She burst out laughing as he slunk away to mend his wounded pride.

From that day on, whenever Wildcat happened to see Jackal, she took refuge in the nearest tree, for Jackal never forgot how she had seen his cowardice, and his desire for revenge was truly something to fear.

How Jackal got his Markings

(A Hottentot story)

The Hottentot used to tell how eventually even the Creator became angry at the slyness of Jackal, and at the way he would always torment the other animals with his tricks. So the Creator decided to punish him. He appeared before Jackal one day, disguised as a young boy.

The "boy" persuaded Jackal to give him a ride on his back. He said that he was lost, and was too tired to walk any further. If Jackal would help him to find his village, he said, he would reward him with a tender young goat when they got there.

So Jackal allowed the "boy" to climb upon his back, and set off, already planning to himself how he could trick the "boy" into giving him not only one goat, but the whole herd.

Suddenly, he felt the "boy's" legs grip his back with a terrible force. "I am the Creator!" cried the "boy," and he produced a ball of fire. "And this is my punishment to you for all your wicked ways!" So saying, He struck Jackal on his flanks with the fire, which set the animal's coat ablaze.

Jackal begged for mercy, but the Creator disappeared, leaving the ball of fire on Jackal's back. Jackal rolled desperately, and finally managed to put out the flames. Then he went on his way, much shaken and humbled.

And that is why, to this day, the jackal has black marks along his body, and silver "ashes" on his back — so that all the animals can see that he was punished by the Creator for his wicked ways.

The Day Jackal Fooled the King of Beasts

(A Zulu story)

This is a Zulu folk tale, and shows exactly the sort of thing that clever old Jackal would get up to.

One day long ago, Jackal was trotting through a narrow and rocky pass when he came face to face with Lion, who was coming in the opposite direction. Realizing that he was too near to escape, Jackal was afraid, for he had played many tricks on Lion in the past, and now Lion might take this opportunity to get his revenge.

In a flash, he thought of a plan. He cowered down on the cliff path, looked above him, and cried, "Help!"

Lion stopped short in surprise. He had indeed been just about to leap upon Jackal and give him the beating of his life.

"Help!" cried Jackal again, "The rocks are about to fall on us! We shall both be crushed! Do something, O mighty Lion!"

Lion looked up too, most alarmed, but before he had time to think, Jackal was begging him to use his great strength to hold up an overhanging rock.

"Hold on!" cried Jackal, "I'll run and fetch that log over there to prop under the rock — then we'll both be saved!"

Lion put his great shoulder to the rock and heaved. While sneering Jackal made his escape, Lion was left all alone to struggle under the weight of the unmoving rock.

How long he remained there before he realized that it had all been yet another trick, we will never know. But one thing is perfectly clear: Jackal had to be twice as wary of Lion from that day forward.

FACTS ABOUT JACKALS
SPECIES:
BLACK-BACKED JACKAL
(Canis mesomelas)
Live singly or, more commonly, in pairs.

	Male	Female
Height	16 in	15 in
Weight	22 lb	18 lb
Weight at Birth	7 oz	7 oz
Age at Weaning	2 months	2 months
Age at Maturity	12 months	8 months
Gestation Period	—	2 months
Number of Young	—	2-6
Lifespan	10 years	10 years

Identification Not unlike a European fox, though larger and taller, the black-backed jackal is easily distinguished from other jackals by the broad black-and-white patch over its back, which is clearly defined from the yellowish covering on the flanks and legs. It has a bushy tail with a black brush and large, pointed, erect ears.

Habitat Open grassland and lightly-treed country.

Habits Jackals are common all over Africa. They are mostly nocturnal and their distinctive, rather friendly howling call can often be heard at dusk or just after. They are very wily animals and run quickly and lightly. They live with a mate or alone, and hunt from a lair in a sheltered hole, usually near water.

They are "true" dogs, with five toes on the front feet and four on the back. Some zoologists believe many domestic dogs are descended from them.

Diet Jackals scavenge and hunt. They eat such things as small rats, ground-nesting birds and their eggs and chicks; reptiles, fat insects and fruit. They will also kill newly born antelopes left unattended by the mother; and attack young livestock, so farmers regard them as pests to be shot, though they have their good side, keeping down pests like rats. They are often seen waiting for lions to finish eating so they can clean up the remains. The more venturesome will try and dart in to steal tidbits from under the lion's nose! Their clever ways have been the subject of many tales throughout Africa.

Breeding Usually no more than six pups are born. The parents hide them in holes in the ground and crevices in rocks. Both parents forage at the weaning stage and provide them with regurgitated, semi-digested food.

Elephant Learns some Manners

(A Shona story)

One day Elephant came across Squirrel on the path to the river. The proud and lordly Elephant swept Squirrel off the path with his trunk, rumbling, "Out of my way, you of no importance and tiny size."

Squirrel was most offended, as he had every right to be. Stamping his little feet in a rage, he decided that he was going to try and teach Elephant some manners.

"Ho!" shouted Squirrel indignantly, "you may be very tall, and you may be very proud, and I bet you think you're the greatest animal on earth, but you're much mistaken!"

Elephant looked round in surprise. "I am not mistaken, Squirrel," he rumbled, "I am the greatest, and everyone knows it."

"Let me tell you something, Elephant," said Squirrel, chittering angrily and flicking his tail, "I may be small, but I can eat ten times as much as you! I challenge you to an eating contest — and I bet you that I, Squirrel, can eat more palm nuts, and for a longer time, than you, high and mighty Elephant!"

Elephant roared with laughter. He was so amused, in fact, that he accepted the tiny creature's challenge. Besides, he was rather fond of palm nuts.

So both animals collected a huge pile of palm nuts and agreed to start the contest the very next morning, at first light. Elephant could hardly wait. He even skipped his evening meal of acacia pods so as to be truly empty for the morning. He intended to put Squirrel firmly in his place, once and for all.

The next day dawned fine and sunny, as it often does in Africa, and the two contestants started to eat.

Elephant munched steadily through his pile, with a fine appetite. Squirrel, nibbling away furiously, was soon full to bursting. Quietly, he slipped away, sending a cousin who was hiding nearby to take his place. Elephant was so absorbed in his greedy task that he didn't even notice. Brothers, sisters, cousins, uncles, aunts — one hungry squirrel after another took a turn at the pile of palm nuts.

Eventually, at midday, Elephant looked up. "Well, Squirrel, have you had enough yet?" he asked, surprised to see his small adversary still busily eating. Not only was he still eating, but his pile of palm nuts was disappearing almost as fast as Elephant's own.

"Not yet!" mumbled Squirrel, his mouth full, "and you?"

"Never!" replied Elephant scornfully. And he started to eat a little faster.

By the time the sun was setting, Elephant was so full he could hardly stand. He looked over to where Squirrel (the original squirrel, who had come back after a day of sleeping in a nearby tree), was still eating more palm nuts. Elephant groaned.

"Truly you are amazing, Squirrel," he said. "I cannot go on, and I'm forced to admit that you have won the contest." And he lifted his trunk in salute.

Squirrel, hopping with delight, thanked Elephant and told him not to be so proud in future. And from that day to this, Elephant has always shown great respect for Squirrel.

The Elephant and the Rain

(An ancient Bushman story)

There were once two great powers in the natural world: Elephant, and the Spirit of Rain. Now Elephant, who as you know was proud and boastful, was always arguing with Rain, trying to make him agree that of the two of them, he, Elephant, was the greater.

One day they were arguing as usual, when the Rain Spirit said, in his wet, gurgling voice, "How can you, Elephant, be a greater power than I, when it is I who nourishes you?"

Elephant was far too proud to admit that Rain was right. Indeed, he didn't even think before replying, "You do not feed me! I find my food for myself. I am my own master in all things."

Rain, angered in earnest this time, decided to act, instead of arguing any further. He turned dark gray, thundered, and said, "If I go away, will you not die?" And then he vanished.

Once Rain had departed, Elephant laughed loudly and said to himself, "Ha! Now I may rule alone. Rain has admitted defeat by running away!"

For many months, Elephant lorded it over the plains and forests, and life continued normally. In fact, it was quite peaceful without the constant loud quarrels of Elephant and Rain.

Then the time of year for the rains arrived. Many of the animals were full with their unborn young ones. Every animal was looking forward to the flush of green grass, and clean, flowing rivers once again.

But, of course, Rain had gone away. The skies remained hot and bright blue. Not even a cloud was seen for weeks. The animals became worried because their newborn young were starving.

In great distress, they went to find Elephant, for was he not their Lord? Elephant looked a bit uncomfortable, but he replied to their demands by saying, "I will call Vulture, the most potent of all the rainmakers."

Elephant then called Vulture and commanded him to cast lots and make rain. But Vulture was Rain's servant, and knew about the quarrel that the two mighty ones had had. He excused himself, explaining to Elephant that he was too afraid of the great Elephant to try, in case he failed.

Elephant then summoned Crow, the wisest of all birds, and commanded her to cast lots to make rain. This she did, and some rain fell. Enough rain fell to fill a few pans, but soon they all dried up, except one, the deepest.

Elephant claimed this last waterhole for himself, and ordered Tortoise to guard it for him while he was away feeding during the day (food was becoming rather difficult to find). Tortoise settled down to guard the pan.

Soon, a herd of giraffe came down to drink and asked Tortoise for water, for they had searched all day and found none. But Tortoise had to refuse, saying the pan was the property of Lord Elephant. Zebras, gemsbok, wildebeest, tsessebe, springboks and many other animals were all in turn refused a drink. They moved off in distance, whispering among themselves and wondering what was to become of them.

In the evening, Lion came down to drink and, as before, Tortoise told him he could not as the pan belonged to Elephant. But Lion was not impressed. He simply cuffed Tortoise out of the way and drank his fill. Poor

Tortoise was helpless, as the other animals, made desperate by thirst, followed Lion's example. They crowded around the pan and drank deeply.

When Elephant returned, the animals had drunk the pan dry, leaving only a mass of churned-up mud. He trumpeted in rage, and turned upon the unfortunate Tortoise. Poor Tortoise tried to explain that he had been too little and weak to stop the thirsty animals, but Elephant was in such a rage that he picked up Tortoise and swallowed him whole.

Now Tortoise did not want to die, especially since he did not deserve such punishment. As soon as he reached Elephant's stomach, he began to tear at the soft insides, determined to get out.

Elephant screamed with pain, and realized at the same time that his pride and arrogance had led him to a nasty end. By the time Tortoise managed to get out, Elephant was dead. Tortoise scuttled off as fast as he could, and ever since, he has refused to answer to anyone. He is his own master, and he goes wherever he likes.

The Rain Spirit, seeing that the tragic lesson had been learned by all the animals, took pity on the thirsty earth and poured down in a deluge, so that all the rivers and pans filled up again.

FACTS ABOUT ELEPHANTS
SPECIES:
AFRICAN ELEPHANT *(Loxodonta africana)*
Males often solitary. Females live in family groups and temporary herds of up to 200.

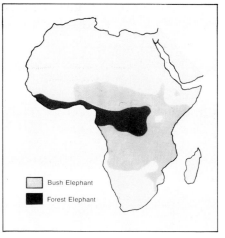

Bush Elephant

Forest Elephant

	Male	Female
Height	10 ft	9 ft
Weight	11000 lb	7700 lb
Weight at Birth	264 lb	264 lb
Age at Weaning	2 years	2 years
Age at Maturity	16 years	14 years
Gestation Period	—	22 months
Number of Young	—	1
Lifespan	55 years	70 years

Identification Elephants are the largest land animals in the world and it is interesting to note the difference between African and Asian elephants: the latter is smaller in stature, has much smaller ears and only the males have tusks. Also, Asian elephants can be tamed and used to work and entertain. These things have not been done successfully with African elephants.

Female African elephants are smaller than the males, with smaller tusks.

Habitat Elephants can be found in grassy, open woodland, deep forest and quite high on the slopes of mountains as long as the ground is not too steep and broken.

Habits Highly organized socially, they live in family groups of 10-20, each ruled by a mature female.

When young bulls are old enough to look after themselves, they form separate temporary "bachelor" herds and fight among themselves to establish the strongest which will eventually return to the family herds to find a mate. This ensures only the strongest animals become fathers. The old bulls often live singly or in pairs and never rejoin the herd.

Family herds will join together in large groups at times of drought, and migrate together. Herds often travel great distances at night and spend a great deal of their time feeding. Elephants love water and are good swimmers. An adult will consume 22 gallons (100 litres) at one time! After their daily drink, they will spend an hour or two splashing, spraying water with their trunks, playing and wallowing in the mud, frequently dusting themselves with fine sand, in much the same way as we use talcum powder!

Elephants will dig deep holes in dry riverbeds, waiting patiently for the water to seep through to give a trunkful to drink. This is useful to other animals, which use the holes after the elephants.

The elephant's trunk is a marvelous tool used for feeding, drinking, stripping bark, smelling the air, picking fruit, and many other things. It is also a formidable weapon if need be, though a mature elephant has no natural enemies. A charging elephant can reach speeds of 25 miles per hour (40 km per hour) over short distances.

Diet Elephants graze and browse, going through up to 660 lbs (300 kg) of food a day, mostly grass. They also eat a variety of leaves, flowers, fruit, roots and tree bark, and in a normal lifespan will grow six sets of teeth! Their habit of pushing over trees to reach a few mouthfuls of young green leaves at the top (or roots at the bottom) can make them wasteful feeders.

Breeding When birth is imminent the cow leaves the herd, often with two or three attendant cows who help look after the baby until it is strong enough to walk back to the herd with its mother after a few days.

Why Rhino scatters his Dung

(A Batonka story)

In days long ago, when animals could talk, Elephant used to tease Rhino about his nearsightedness and bad temper (which was not very fair, since Elephant himself has not got the world's best eyesight, nor is he the most sweet-tempered of Africa's characters). Anyway, Elephant was teasing Rhino and sure enough, after a while Rhino could not help himself — he lost his temper. He challenged Elephant to a contest. (Rhino was quite sure he could win, and so prove that he was better than Elephant in at least one way.) The contest was to see who could produce the largest dung-heap.

Now both animals are large, they both eat vast quantities of vegetation each day, and of course they both make a lot of dung. But Rhino made by far the largest heap, as old Elephant soon found out.

Rhino's pride at beating Elephant was short-lived, however. Elephant was a poor loser, and he flew into a jealous rage that was worse than anything even Rhino had been known to have. In his fury, he attacked Rhino and beat him savagely with his trunk, goring him with his tusks until Rhino begged for mercy.

"O Elephant," pleaded Rhino, "Stop! I was mistaken. You are the greatest of creatures. You win. Only stop!" Poor Rhino lay on his back in the dust, wailing in fear.

Gradually, Elephant's great fury began to wear off, and he made Rhino beg and plead and promise never again to challenge the might of the Lord of the Beasts, namely himself, Elephant. At last he was satisfied and let poor Rhino escape.

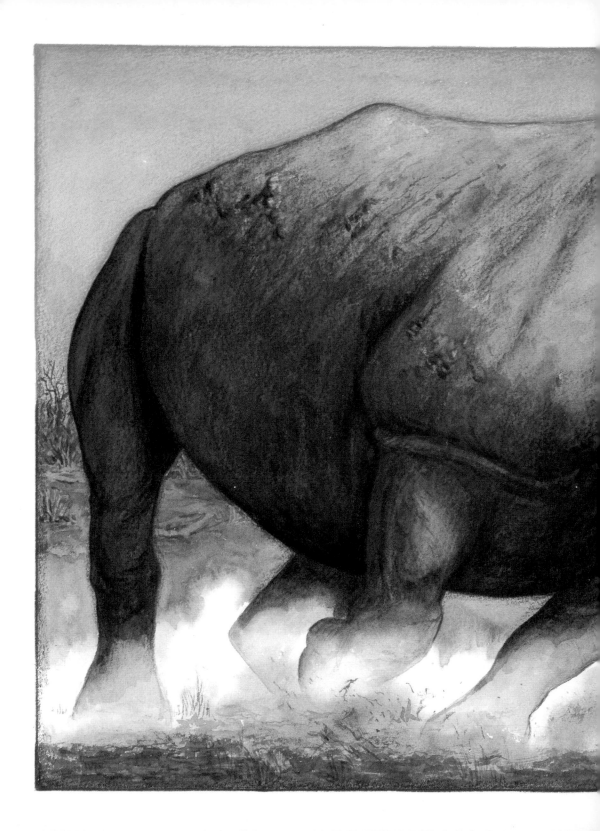

Rhino never forgot that dreadful beating, and he is afraid he may receive another one, so he makes sure that his dung-heap always looks smaller than that of Elephant. And this is why he kicks at it, scattering it until it is quite flat.

The Lost Quill

(A Ndebele story)

Once, in ancient times, Elephant and Rhino had a little argument which led to a big fight (both were short-tempered animals, as you now well know). Rhino fought bravely and wounded Elephant several times with his sharp horn; but his bad temper and rage made him fight rather blindly.

Elephant, however, kept his temper under control and, because he was much bigger and stronger, and could use his long tusks, he was soon winning. Eventually, Rhino had to give in. Bruised and torn, with a great many gashes in his thick hide, he limped away.

Rhino was in great pain, and bleeding badly. He sought out Porcupine, whom he thought might be able to help him. He begged her to give him one of her longest and strongest quills so that he could use it as a needle and sew up the great tears in his skin.

Porcupine, who was not too happy about being awakened from her daytime sleep, was anxious to get back to bed, and so to get rid of Rhino she agreed to lend him her best quill on one condition: that Rhino would return it when he had finished with it. She also felt rather sorry for Rhino.

"My quills," she squeaked, "are all I have to protect me against my enemy, Lion. So I am depending on you, Rhino, to bring that quill back."

Rhino solemnly agreed to this and gave her his word that he would return the quill the very next day.

Rhino sewed up his torn skin, using fiber from a baobab tree. (To this day, you can still see the rough, scarred ridges on his hide.) Satisfied with his handiwork, he lay down in some soft grass for a much-needed, healing sleep. He placed Porcupine's quill carefully beside him for safekeeping.

One evening a few days later, Rhino happened to meet Porcupine. He suddenly remembered his promise, but try as he might, he just couldn't remember where he had left the quill, or what had become of it. All he remembered was sewing himself up with the quill held in his mouth. "Goodness me!" he thought, "Could I have swallowed it by mistake?"

After a great deal of thought, Rhino came to the conclusion that if he had swallowed the quill, then sooner or later it would meet the same fate as all the other things that he swallowed each day. He explained all this to Porcupine, and apologized, promising soon to return the quill.

And that is why Rhino began to kick his dung about: he has been searching ever since in the hope of finding that lost porcupine quill among his droppings.

FACTS ABOUT RHINOCEROS
SPECIES:
WHITE RHINOCEROS (Ceratotherium simum, syn. Diceros simus)

Males often solitary. Several females may form a herd with a dominant bull. These herds of up to 10 are called a "laager".

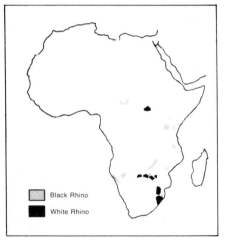

Black Rhino
White Rhino

	Male	Female
Height	6 ft	5⅓ ft
Weight	6600 lb	4400 lb
Weight at Birth	88 lb	88 lb
Age at Weaning	2 years	2 years
Age at Maturity	7 years	5 years
Gestation Period	—	18 months
Number of Young	—	1
Lifespan	45 years	45 years

BLACK RHINOCEROS (Diceros bicornis) Solitary. ENDANGERED SPECIES.

	Male	Female		Male	Female
Height	4⅔ ft	4 ft	Age at Maturity	7 years	5 years
Weight	3300 lb	2200 lb	Gestation Period	—	17 months
Weight at Birth	88 lb	77 lb	Number of Young	—	1
Age at Weaning	2 years	2 years	Lifespan	40 years	40 years

Identification Contrary to what their names would lead you to believe, both black and white rhinoceros have a slate-gray, very thick skin, heavily folded round the neck and are hairless except for the tip of the tail and the edges of the ears, which are fringed with thick bristles. The only variation in color comes from the mud or dust in which they've been wallowing.

The big difference between them is that the black rhino has a pointed, flexible upper lip which enables it to graze leaves and twigs — thus it is a *browser*. The white rhino has a square upper lip and grazes on grass. This results in their characteristic postures — the black moving with head held up and the white with it lowered. The white rhino also has a massive hump on its neck and is the larger of the two. In fact, next to the elephant, it is the largest living land mammal.

The two horns are similar in both and there is little apparent difference between male and female. The horns, which are normally grown by both sexes, do not consist of bone but of hair fused into a hard, bone-like substance. A by-product of these horns is an aphrodisiac much sought after in parts of Asia. Consequently, the animals have long been hunted and are now on the list of endangered species.

Habitat Open tree and bush savannah, thorn scrub and the lower slopes of mountains.

Habits Living mainly alone or in small family groups, the rhino is very territorial. Its home range always includes at least one waterhole, preferably with a mud-wallow. On the boundaries each male leaves dung-heaps at regular intervals. He visits these frequently to deposit more droppings which are scattered about with the hind legs and front horn to form a flattened patch, sometimes more than six feet (two metres) across. The probable reason for this is to warn other males that they are trespassing, and to advertise his own presence to single females who may thus be encouraged to enter his territory.

The two species of rhinoceros have different characters. The black rhino is short-tempered and will charge an intruder without much provocation. White rhinos are generally more docile, although they should still be treated with respect. Rhinoceros feed mainly in early morning and late afternoon and frequently drink at night.

Diet As already explained, the white rhino eats grasses almost exclusively and the black rhino usually browses on twigs and leaves.

Breeding There is no particular breeding season, and single offspring are produced at intervals of rarely less than three years.

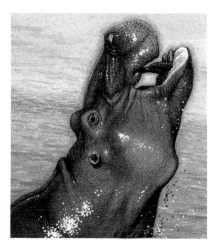

No Fish for the Hippo

(A Bushman story)

This is a story about why Hippo scatters his dung about. The story is common to most tribes of Africa, although it started with the Bushman.

When the Creator was giving each animal a place in the world, the pair of hippos begged to be allowed to live in the cool water which they so dearly loved.

The Creator looked at them, and was doubtful about letting them live in the water: their mouths were so large, their teeth so long and sharp, and their size and their appetites were so big, He was afraid that they would eat up all the fish. Besides, He had already granted the place to another predator — the crocodile. He couldn't have two kinds of large, hungry animals living in the rivers. So the Creator refused the hippos' request, and told them that they could live out on the open plains.

At this news, the two hippos began to weep and wail, making the most awful noise. They pleaded and pleaded with the Creator, who finally gave in. But He made the hippos promise that if they lived in the rivers, they must never harm a single fish. They were to eat grass instead. The Hippos promised solemnly, and rushed to the river, grunting with delight.

And to this day, hippos always scatter their dung on the river bank, so the Creator can see that it contains no fish bones. And you can still hear them laughing with joy that they were allowed to live in the rivers after all.

When Hippo was Hairy

(A Ndebele story)

The Ndebele have a story which explains why the hippo stays in the water all day and only comes out to feed at night. It goes like this:

Long, long ago hippos did not live in rivers and pools; they lived in the bush with other herd animals. In those days, Hippo had a very fine coat of glossy, chestnut-brown hair. He also had silky, soft ears and a beautiful bushy tail, of which he was overly proud.

Every day at noon when he had his drink, he would spend hours gazing at his own reflection in the water, turning this way and that to admire himself from every angle. His vanity was so great that he demanded that all the other animals should praise his beauty.

One day, when he was at the water's edge admiring his own reflection, he said to himself, "Oh, how handsome I am! Not a bit like that stupid Hare, with his coarse coat, long ears and silly twitchy nose. What a ridiculously short tail he has, and how clumsily he hops!"

Unfortunately for Hippo, Hare just happened to be nearby and he overheard what Hippo was saying. He was furious. He decided that Hippo needed to learn humility.

After thinking for a while, Hare collected a large pile of soft, dry grass under a large umbrella tree. He offered it to Hippo, saying, "O magnificent Hippo! Here is a warm bed that I have prepared for you, since winter is on its way and the nights are growing cold."

Hippo accepted the gift condescendingly and gave Hare a haughty nod. "Yes, Hare," he said, "I must be looked after. I am glad to see that you realize your responsibilities!"

Hare nearly choked with rage. What a vain creature Hippo was! "Just you wait, my fine friend," he thought to himself. And he helped Hippo to settle down comfortably.

Then Hare ran to a nearby village. While everyone in the village was busy drinking beer, he crept up to the cooking fire and stole some glowing embers. He carried them off on a piece of broken clay-pot.

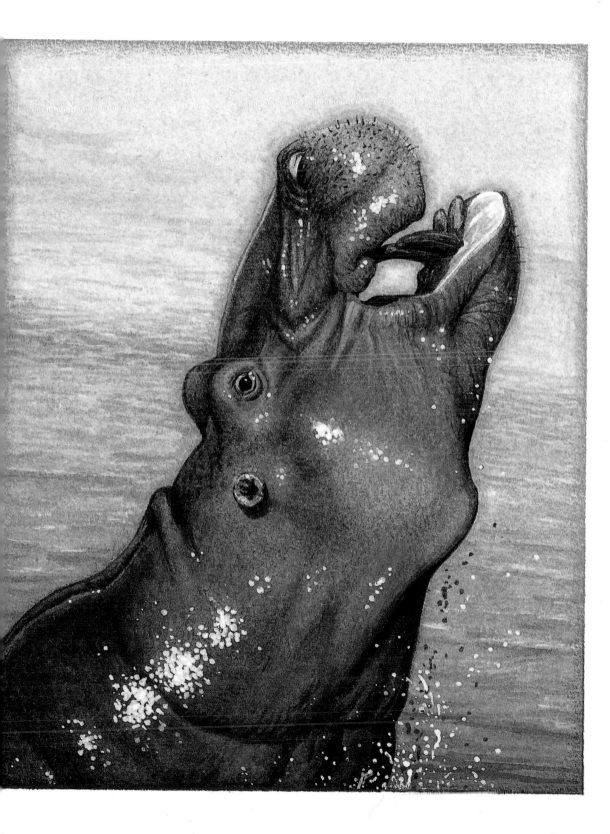

Hippo was snoring happily in his warm bed of dry grass when Hare got back. Hare crept up and threw in the burning embers, blowing on them until he had a fine blaze going. Poor Hippo awoke to find that his fine coat of fur was on fire! He heard Hare laughing nastily as he dashed off out of the way.

Hippo was confused and terrified, and at first he just thrashed about, trying to beat out the flames. Soon, however, the fire reached his skin, and in agony he charged away towards the waterhole. As he crashed through the bush, the fire spread to the dry winter grass and soon the whole area was ablaze.

Hippo reached the water just in time to save his life. The flames were put out and the cool water soothed his pain. The fire raged around the water's edge and Hippo had to hold his breath and sink beneath the surface. Only his eyes and nostrils showed when he came up for air.

The bushfire burned for a long time, but at last it died out. Hippo climbed out of the pool. He felt stiff, and sore, but he was very much alive. He

was going to find Hare and give him the beating of his life.

But Hippo couldn't resist his habit of pausing to look at himself in the pool. He got a terrible shock. Reflected in the water was a pinky-gray, wrinkled, bald creature. He could not believe his eyes. His lovely bushy tail was gone, all his hair had been burned off, and ugly, round, pink ears poked out where his long silky ones used to be. Without the fine glossy fur his legs looked short and stubby, and his flanks bulged with fat.

Hippo was horrified. He was ashamed, broken-hearted and, most of all, embarrassed. He rushed straight back into the water to hide his body from curious eyes. Weeping with shame at his dreadful appearance, he sank below the surface so that only his nostrils and eyes showed.

And there he has remained ever since. Hippo is now a creature of rivers and lakes. Only at night, when no one can see him, does he come out to walk and graze at the edge of the forest. Although he is still vain at heart, it happened so long ago that today hardly anyone remembers how Hippo once was hairy.

FACTS ABOUT HIPPOPOTAMUS
SPECIES:
HIPPOPOTAMUS *(Hippopotamus amphibius)*
Gregarious, living in herds of up to 20.

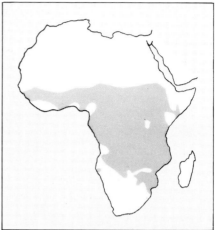

	Male	Female
Height	5 ft	4 ft
Weight	6600 lb	4400 lb
Weight at Birth	66 lb	66 lb
Age at Weaning	12 months	12 months
Age at Maturity	7 years	4 years
Gestation Period	—	8 months
Number of Young	—	1
Lifespan	30 years	30 years

Identification The hippopotamus is unmistakable: massive and ugly, with a very large head, wide squarish muzzle, "periscope" eyes, small ears, narrow nostrils which are closed under water, and short legs. Color varies from dark brown to grayish black, with pink around the eyes, sides of the face and underbelly.

Habitat Rivers, swamps and lakes bordered by vegetation.

Habits The name "hippopotamus" is derived from two Greek words meaning "horse" and "river." Hippopotamus spend most of their time in or close to water, during the day wallowing together in the shallows and backwaters or lying on sandbanks in the sun. At night they leave the water to graze and may travel far distances to find food. If alarmed they will bolt straight back to the water, scattering everything in their path, so it is unwise to get between them and the water!

They can stay beneath the water for 4 or 5 minutes at a time. If molested, they will raise just their nostrils above the water. Sometimes the whole head breaks the surface and water sprays about from the nostrils, accompanied by a roar-like bellow. Excellent swimmers, they can also walk well on the river or lake bed because of their weight. Consequently they play an important part in the ecology of river banks and swamps by keeping water channels open.

Diet Hippos are vegetarian, eating mostly grass and fine reeds which they crop very efficiently with their extremely hard lips.

Breeding Birth takes place on land, with usually a single calf. Hippos are good mothers, taking care to chase crocodiles away from the area where they keep their young, and teaching them to swim and wallow. They carry the very young calves on their backs in the water.

The Days of the Hunting Buffalo

(A Bushman story)

In ancient Bushman lore, the buffalo was once a meat eater,
and a much feared hunter.

There was once a particular Buffalo, a huge and fierce bull who lived near the great swamps. He was a hunter of great strength and skill, and had a huge appetite which all the animals feared. So fierce was he that only the great Elephant and Rhino were safe from his deadly attacks.

One day, Buffalo caught Lion unawares while he was drinking at a pan. Buffalo was about to kill Lion with one sweep of his mighty horns, when Lion begged for mercy. Buffalo agreed to spare his life on one condition: that Lion would become his slave, and hunt food for Buffalo. Of course Lion agreed. What choice did he have?

So Buffalo commanded Lion to catch a fat springbok which was grazing on the other side of the pan. Lion obeyed, and dragged the prize back to Buffalo, who enjoyed a nice, easy meal. Buffalo thought to himself, "Well! This is a most excellent arrangement! I will now have time to enjoy my afternoon wallow, and sleep in the shade whenever I want!"

The next day, Buffalo called Lion again and ordered him to catch a tender young zebra, as he was hungry for his breakfast. Lion soon returned with

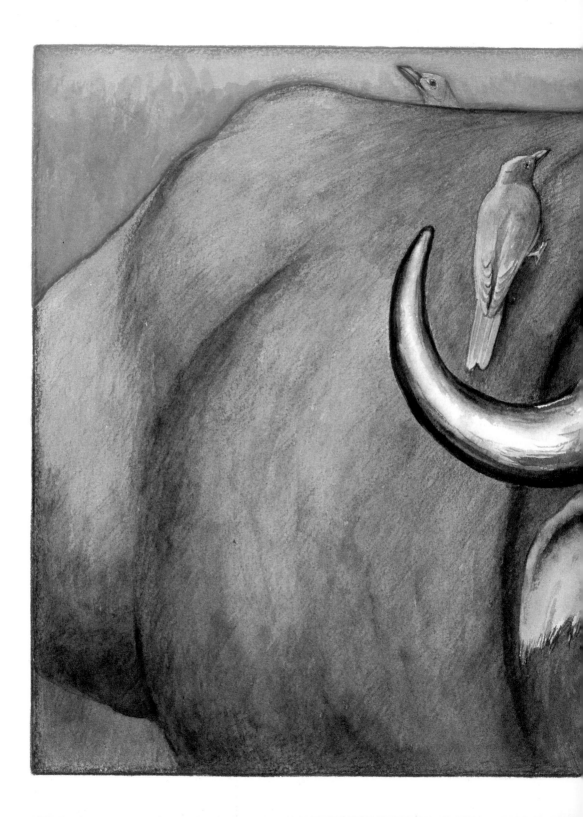

the catch and Buffalo greedily devoured the whole zebra. He didn't leave a scrap for Lion, not even a bone to reward him for his work.

After that, Buffalo found Lion every day and ordered him to kill more and more animals in order to satisfy his greed. Not once was there a morsel left for Lion.

Meanwhile, because their pride leader was spending all his time hunting for Buffalo, Lion's wives and cubs were beginning to find it difficult to hunt, and some of the cubs were starving. As the pride grew thinner and weaker, Buffalo grew fatter and greedier. After a while he was eating five times a day. Poor Lion wore himself out supplying food for dreadful Buffalo.

One day Buffalo found Lion lying wearily beneath a shady thorn tree. He ordered him to get up and prepare for a great hunt. Because of his easy life, Buffalo was now so huge and fat he could hardly walk. He had also developed a most astounding appetite.

"Today, Lion," said Buffalo, "you will go out and kill me one of every kind of animal in the bush!"

All at once, Lion knew that this was too much — an impossible task, especially as he was almost worn out. He protested: "O mighty one! Be reasonable! Even I could not manage such a thing." And he shook his great black mane in anger. "Do you not see my family? They are starving because I never have time to help them with the hunt. I beg of you, Great Buffalo, release me from my promise."

But Buffalo's greed was enormous, and he had no pity. "I spared your life!" he roared, "Now you must do my bidding if you value your honor!" And he pounded the ground with his enormous front hoof, raising a cloud of dust.

Lion drew himself wearily to his feet. He knew there was no longer any honor in the situation, and had decided to act.

"O Buffalo," he said, "regrettably, I am indeed honor bound to agree to your request. As you command me, through sheer greed, to kill one of every beast in the bush, I shall obey. And I will begin with you!"

So saying, Lion sprang onto Buffalo's enormous back and sank his great teeth into his neck, killing him immediately.

At last, Lion and his family had a huge feast, and after that they took a liking to buffalo meat, and continued to hunt for it whenever possible.

The other buffalo learned the lesson Lion had taught them, and started

to eat grass again. They also decided that it would be safer to live in herds, in order to protect themselves from the King of Beasts.

FACTS ABOUT BUFFALO
SPECIES:
BUFFALO *(Syncerus caffer)*
Males occur in small bachelor herds or are solitary.
Females occur in large herds of 100-1000.
Both sexes have horns.

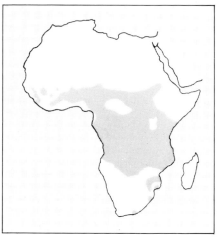

	Male	Female
Height	5⅓ ft	5 ft
Weight	1540 lb	1320 lb
Weight at Birth	88 lb	88 lb
Age at Weaning	12 months	12 months
Age at Maturity	8 years	4 years
Gestation Period	—	11 months
Number of Young	—	1
Lifespan	20 years	20 years

Identification Buffalo look massive, solid, indestructible, and in fact they are enormously strong. Their physique is the same as that of domestic cattle, except for slightly shorter legs and the huge blackish horns growing from a large, flattened, helmet-like plate covering and protecting the top of the head.

Habitat Buffalo can be found in a wide range of terrain, from the lower slopes of mountains to dense forests and open plains, but all habitats must have one feature in common — plenty of water, for buffalo must drink daily.

Habits Buffalo only have one persistent enemy, the lion, preying on the cows and calves and the old solitary bulls — which put up quite a fight! It is not unusual for lions to be killed or severely injured by the bulls. Occasionally buffalo will be taken by a crocodile, for they frequently swim rivers to reach lush vegetation on islands or far banks.

Like so many seemingly dangerous animals, if undisturbed buffalo are docile and harmless. If threatened or frightened, however, they can become fearsome adversaries, despite their relatively poor sight, which they make up for with excellent smell, hearing and cunning intelligence.

Diet Buffalo live mostly on grass and they particularly like the lush, sweet growth in river valleys. In times of drought they will browse on leaves and twigs.

Breeding There is no specific breeding time, though in some places it peaks during the July to September dry season.

The day Baboon outwitted Leopard

(A Zulu story)

Long, long ago, Baboon and Leopard were friends. One day, Leopard had chased Hare (you know why leopards chase hares now, don't you?), until Hare had taken refuge in an anthill. Leopard called her friend Baboon, and asked him to stand guard over the anthill while she went down to the river for a drink.

Baboon agreed, and settled down with his back to the side of the ant-hill, next to the hole where Hare had disappeared. It was a warm day, and fairly close to noon. After a while, Baboon started to doze off and was soon snoring gently.

Hare heard the snores and crept quietly out. As he was leaping away to safety, Leopard came back. She saw Hare disappearing over the hill and, in a rage, she charged up to sleeping Baboon and slapped him awake.

"O worthless monkey!" she roared. (This was a terrible insult, as baboons just hate being called "monkey.") "You have let that fine fat Hare escape. That's my lunch you have lost, you foolish ape!" And her eyes blazed in anger.

Now an angry, hungry leopard is not a very reassuring sight, and Baboon started to back away in fear. Leopard however, had not finished with him. She grabbed the frightened Baboon and was about to scold him even harder, when the feel of warm flesh between her paws suddenly made her stop in mid-sentence. Her eyes gleamed, and she licked her lips. "Hmm... As you have lost me my meal, I think you will do very nicely instead!" And, forgetting their past friendship, she opened her jaws to take a bite.

"Eee!" screamed Baboon. "Wait, O beautiful one! Let me at least pay for my crime in a proper manner. Did you not know, most lovely of beasts, that the best way to kill a baboon is to drop it from a height? We break into many small pieces, making an easy and tender meal for the hunter."

Leopard was amazed. She paused to think. But, seeing her hesitate, Baboon chattered on, leaving her no time to reflect. "Just throw me up into this tree!" he jabbered, "You'll see — I will fall and split open just like a ripe calabash melon!"

Leopard couldn't resist the thought, so she tossed Baboon high into the branches above.

Quick as a flash, Baboon climbed up into the safety of the thickest thorns at the top. He started to laugh. He sat there screaming loud and long abuse at Leopard, calling her every name he could think of, and at the top of his voice. He even called her a mangy cat — and this made her yellow eyes blaze with rage. Other animals were beginning to gather around, attracted by the commotion. Leopard's pride could not stand it, and she bounded off, lashing her tail in fury.

But she never forgot the insults, and she never forgave them. To this day, the leopard hunts the baboon in preference to all other food. And the baboon screams with fear at the very sight of his deadliest enemy.

The Shona tribe of Zimbabwe have a superstition about the baboon. They believe that he is used by evil sorcerers as a "familiar", and can be a messenger. They think that people who are owed things pay the N'ganga (sorcerer) to send the baboon to collect the debt. The baboon then speaks in any language necessary. If the debt owed is in cattle, the baboon will not accept any excuses, and will spirit away the cattle without permission.

The magical powers that the baboon is thought to possess are probably due to the fact that he is so human-looking, but at the same time fierce and crafty.

FACTS ABOUT BABOONS

SPECIES:
CHACMA BABOON *(Papio ursinus)*

Gregarious; live in troops of 10-200.

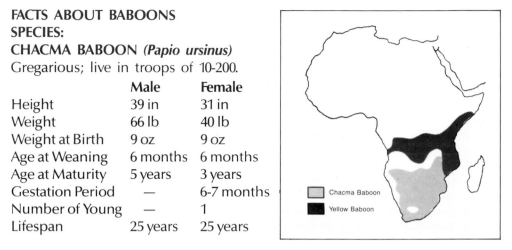

	Male	Female
Height	39 in	31 in
Weight	66 lb	40 lb
Weight at Birth	9 oz	9 oz
Age at Weaning	6 months	6 months
Age at Maturity	5 years	3 years
Gestation Period	—	6-7 months
Number of Young	—	1
Lifespan	25 years	25 years

Chacma Baboon
Yellow Baboon

Identification Baboons are easily distinguished from other monkeys because they are large, with a protruding, squarish muzzle, rather like most dogs. They are covered with a yellowish olive-brown coarse hair which is darker on the top of the head and along the spine and can be up to 1 ft in length.

Habitat Mostly in woodland, particularly in areas of rough country with rocky outcrops.

Habits These large, powerful, highly intelligent monkeys have an organized social life in troops ranging from 10-200 depending upon the availability of food.

Whether nesting, feeding or on the move, the dominant males, mothers and young stay in the center of the troop, while the weaker males, females without young and juveniles nearing maturity feed or play around them, acting as sentinels or as scouts.

It can be fascinating to watch a troop of baboons arrive at a waterhole to drink. The dominant males immediately climb trees or any other vantage point from which they can use their acutely developed eyesight to look for danger. If they see none, they remain silent, and the rest of the troop quickly approach the water. And if there are other animals waiting, such as antelope, which have been too nervous to drink, these will immediately follow the baboons to the water's edge and satisfy their thirst.

Diet Baboons are also like humans because, being omnivorous, they can eat meat, vegetation, fruit and indeed most chewable material. However, the bulk of their diet is vegetarian, mostly grass supplemented by seeds, shoots, tuberous roots and rhizomes which they dig up; buds, flowers, seed pods and fruits.

Breeding Within the troop, there is no family or "harem." When in season, the females present themselves first to the less dominant and then to the dominant males. They breed throughout the year.

Why Giraffe and the Oxpecker are Good Friends

(A Bushman legend)

In ancient times before the coming of man, when all the animals lived together peacefully, a huge bushfire swept through the land, started by a bolt of lightning. The tinder dry grass burst into flames and the strong winds that are common before the rainy season, quickly spread a wall of flames from horizon to horizon. Unable to do anything to put it out, the animals fled in panic before the deadly flames.

A pair of oxpeckers had made their nest in a hole in a tree trunk and had just hatched out their chicks, but the tree stood in the path of the advancing flames. The oxpeckers pleaded with the passing animals to help them rescue their little chicks, but they took no notice as they ran from the deadly flames.

Just when the desperate oxpeckers were about to give up hope, the kind giraffe came along and seeing the birds so distressed asked what was wrong. "Oh Giraffe," the oxpeckers wailed, "Our nest will soon be burned and our chicks with it. Please carry it away from the fire for us."

Giraffe took pity on the oxpeckers in their dreadful plight and rushed to the tree through the dense smoke and the flying sparks. Because of his long legs and neck, Giraffe was able to reach to the top of the tree

and pluck the nest and the young fledglings from the hole and carry them to safety.

"Oh, thank you, thank you, kind Giraffe," said the much relieved oxpeckers, "How can we ever repay you for your kindness?"

"That will be quite easy," replied the Giraffe, "I am always troubled by ticks. If you like you can ride on my back and pick the ticks off for me."

"We will gladly do this service for you for ever and ever," replied the overjoyed oxpeckers.

Today, if you go into the African bush you will nearly always see oxpeckers riding along on Giraffe, crawling over his neck, flanks and even into his ears, meticulously keeping their promise.

Why the Giraffe has a Long Neck

(An East African story)

In the beginning, the Creator gave Giraffe the same legs and neck as all the other animals; in fact Giraffe resembled some of the larger antelope such as Eland and Kudu.

All was well until one year a terrible drought afflicted the land. All the animals began to go hungry, as the best grazing and browsing were eaten. All that remained were the bitter tufts of yellowed turpentine grass and dry, shriveled twigs. There was great competition among the animals and they had to walk many weary miles each day between feeding areas and the few remaining waterholes. In times like these, only the fittest and strongest of the animals could survive.

One day, Giraffe met his friend Rhino out on the scorched plains where the dust-devils whirled and the horizon shimmered in the terrible heat. They trudged wearily along the trail back to the waterhole, and as they walked they complained about the hard times and the lack of food.

"Ah, my friend," said Giraffe, "See how there are too many animals searching out here on the plains — all they do is trample the remaining grass into the dust. And yet look at those tall acacia trees over there."

"OOMPHhh," said Rhino. (He wasn't — and still isn't — a very gifted talker.)

"How lovely it would be," continued Giraffe, "to be able to reach the topmost branches, where the tender green leaves are. Now there you have plenty of food, but I can't climb trees and I don't suppose you could either."

Rhino agreed, squinting nearsightedly up at the beautiful canopy of thick green leaves. "Perhaps," he said, "we could see the Man-Magician." He paused. "He's very wise and powerful." And he nibbled a dry twig, thinking.

"What a good idea!" said Giraffe, "Which way, old friend? Do you think he could help us?" And the two friends set off into the sunset, stopping on the way for a quick drink at the muddy waterhole.

87

After a long and tiring walk through the night and half-way through the next day, Rhino and Giraffe finally found the dwelling of the witchdoctor and explained their problem.

The Man-Magician laughed and said, "Oh, that is fairly easy. Come here tomorrow at noon and I will give you both a magic herb to eat. It will make your legs and your necks grow so long, that you will be able to reach the tree tops!"

The Man-Magician busied himself preparing his magic, and Giraffe and Rhino, both greatly excited, went back to the waterhole.

The next day, only Giraffe was at the witchdoctor's hut at the arranged time. Poor dimwitted Rhino had found a patch of nice green grass which had somehow escaped the notice of the other animals. And, quite forgetting about his noon appointment, he was greedily tucking into his unexpected meal.

After waiting for some time for Rhino to appear, the Man-Magician finally grew impatient. He gave Giraffe all of the magic herbs and disappeared into the shade of his hut. Giraffe ate them all up, and as soon as he had finished, he felt the strangest tingling feeling in his legs and neck. He blinked. The ground was getting further away! What a funny feeling!

Giraffe closed his eyes in half-fear, half-giddiness. Then he opened them again. Oh, how the world had changed! He was high up in the air, he could see for miles! He looked down at his long, long legs and his long, long neck, and smiled. The magic had worked wonderfully well. And there, level with his eyes and not two paces away, was the thick green canopy of a tall acacia tree.

Eventually Rhino remembered where he was supposed to be, and trotted hurriedly up to the witchdoctor's hut. He was too late. He saw the new tall, elegant giraffe browsing from the tree tops to his heart's content, free from the competition of all the other animals. When the Man-Magician told him that there was no magic herb left, Rhino lost his temper. Thinking that the Man-Magician had tricked him, he lowered his great sharp horn and charged, chasing him a long way into the bush.

Some say that to this day, Rhino is always very bad-tempered, and chases people whenever he is reminded of the Giraffe's greatest gift, his long, beautiful neck.

The Giraffe in the Sky

(An ancient Bushman legend)

At the very beginning of time, say the Bushmen, the Sun did not know its way around the heavens. Giraffe had a habit of staring curiously at everything, and so the Creator thought that it would be a good idea to give Giraffe the task of watching over the Sun, so that it didn't go astray.

Giraffe took his job very seriously. (Indeed, he was so good at it that the Sun never again took a wrong turn.) The Creator was very proud of Giraffe, and He decided to honor him. He rearranged a few stars so that they made a giraffe shape in the sky, and you can still see it to this day.

The Bushmen call the pattern Tutwa (Giraffe), and use it to guide them when they travel at night. English-speaking people call Tutwa the Southern Cross, and use it as a guide, too.

FACTS ABOUT GIRAFFES
SPECIES:
GIRAFFE *(Giraffa camelopardalis)*

Males mainly solitary; females form small, loose herds of up to 20.

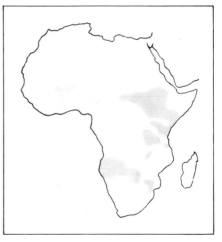

	Male	Female
Height (total)	18 ft	16 ft
Weight	2640 lb	1980 lb
Weight at Birth	220 lb	220 lb
Age at Weaning	6 months	6 months
Age at Maturity	5 years	4 years
Gestation Period	—	15 months
Number of Young	—	1
Lifespan	20 years	20 years

Identification No animal could be easier to identify than the giraffe, with its enormously long neck. It is the tallest animal in the world, reaching up to 18 feet (5.5 m). It has seven vertebrae in the neck, the same as other mammals, but they are very elongated. The two horns are really bony growths covered with skin and hair except at the tip. Both sexes have horns, and there is also a curious bony growth between the eyes. The coat varies somewhat in color and pattern but is generally reddish-brown in irregular patches divided by white to light fawn lines.

Habitat Giraffes live in open grassland country with light bush and acacia. They are never found in heavily forested country.

Habits The long neck, developed over countless thousands of years, enables the giraffe to browse on the topmost branches of the trees of the plains so that it does not have to compete with other browsing animals for food. This also enables the giraffe to see danger a long way off; other browsing and grazing animals therefore tend to stay close, using it as a sentinel. Any signs of nervousness from the giraffe and the others run off.

Its long slender legs allow it to run very fast — 30 miles per hour (50 km per hour) — and although the rather stiff-legged gait may seem ungainly at first sight, as the swaying rhythm develops, a galloping giraffe becomes a majestic sight. The legs are also the giraffe's only means of defense. It either kicks out brutally with the rear legs (and has been known to kill lions in this way), or rears up and chops down very hard with the sharp front hooves.

Giraffes are most vulnerable to attack when drinking, for they have to splay their legs right out in order to lower their heads to reach the water. It is difficult for them to get up quickly and lions quite often catch them in that position by leaping on their backs. When that happens, they have been observed galloping through thick bush in an attempt to knock the attacker off; their skin is extremely tough and remains unharmed by the thorns and branches. Generally, however, only young giraffes fall victim to lions.

Diet Giraffes browse on a wide variety of tall trees, eating leaves and shoots from the highest branches. As well as the long neck, they are aided by a long, prehensile upper lip and a tongue that can be extended some distance from the mouth. When water is available they drink frequently, but can live for long periods without it.

Breeding There is no special breeding season. Usually only one calf is born and starts to browse on its own at the relatively young age of a couple of weeks. Younger giraffes are left in a "nursery" group by day while their mothers go off to feed.

Why Waterbuck helped Crocodile

(A Makushu story from the Okavango)

Long ago, after the coming of man who brought hunting to the Earth, all the animals were afraid of Lion. He was the greatest hunter of all; even man was afraid of his strength and skills.

In these early days, Waterbuck lived in small herds and mixed with the other animals of the plains. When Lion was hunting, Waterbuck, like the other animals, would flee from him; none but mighty Elephant could hope to defend himself against such strength and ferocity. Lion was very fast and hunted together in prides so many animals, great and small, fell to the King of Beasts.

One day Waterbuck had to flee for his life when his herd was attacked by Lion, but after a long chase Waterbuck was lucky enough to escape. He had run such a long way he had left the plains behind and saw for the first time a vast area of swamps and forests. Wandering through the reed beds and huge forests of waterberry and fig trees, Waterbuck decided that this would be a good place to live; lots of food, plenty of water and, most important of all, plenty of cover to hide from Lion.

Suddenly Waterbuck heard wails and cries for help. Near the water's edge a huge crocodile had been trapped beneath a fallen branch and was unable to move. Seeing Waterbuck he called, "Please help me, I beg you. As you can see I am trapped and will surely die from starvation."

Now Waterbuck knew all about the sly, cunning Crocodile who was as feared a hunter of the waters as Lion was of the plains. Waterbuck felt pity for Crocodile and decided to help, but first he said, "For all your strength, O Great Scaly One, you will surely die should I walk away. Yet I will save you provided you agree to one condition."

"Name what you will, O Merciful One; for the gift of my life I am bound to honor your desire," pleaded Crocodile.

"In return for your life you will allow me to enter the water at will, whether to cool off in the summer heat or to escape from my enemies. You, Crocodile, must leave me in peace in your domain."

To this Crocodile gladly agreed, and Waterbuck set about freeing the huge reptile. Although the branch was thick and a great weight, Waterbuck managed to use his horns as a lever to pry the log up, allowing Crocodile to slither free.

As Crocodile was about to swim off Waterbuck said, "Remember your promise, Scaly One; I have proven my great strength to you. All would not go well with you should you break your word."

Crocodile vowed to keep his word and swam off, thanking Waterbuck for his kindness.

To this day when Waterbuck is chased by Lion he runs to the safety of water (most members of the cat family hate getting wet and do not chase prey into deep water). Waterbuck knows he is safe from attack by Crocodile, thanks to his act of kindness, and perhaps Crocodile is just a little bit scared of the strength of Waterbuck.

How the Waterbuck got its White Circle

One dark night, when there was no moon, a waterbuck mother and her young ones grazed very close to a tribesman's hut. This man had been busy whitewashing the walls of his hut in preparation for a visit by a relative, and he had left the pots of whitewash outside.

One of the waterbuck accidentally knocked over the pots in the dark, making such a noise that the tribesman woke up. He ran outside and was very angry to see that all of his nice white paint had been spilled. He shouted at the buck, and chased them. The waterbuck scattered and ran in all directions.

In his anger, the tribesman picked up a pot and threw it at the mother waterbuck. It struck her firmly on the hindquarters, and left a large white circle on her rump. Now this was very useful, because it showed up nicely in the dark, and her young ones were able to follow her to the safety of the forest.

When the waterbuck realized what a useful thing it was to have a white ring around their bottoms, they decided to keep it, and from that day to this, no self-respecting waterbuck has been without one.

FACTS ABOUT WATERBUCK

SPECIES:
COMMON WATERBUCK
(Kobus ellipsiprymus)
Found in small herds of up to 20.
Only the male has horns.

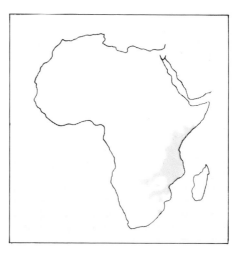

	Male	Female
Height	4⅓ ft	4 ft
Weight	550 lb	440 lb
Weight at Birth	18 lb	18 lb
Age at Weaning	9 months	9 months
Age at Maturity	2 years	2 years
Gestation Period	—	8 months
Number of Young	—	1
Lifespan	10 years	10 years

Identification Common waterbuck are big, strong-looking antelopes, the males carrying two long, heavily ringed horns angled backwards and sweeping gently out, up and finally becoming perpendicular. Coats are coarse, reddish or grayish-brown in color, with a shaggy mane around the neck of both male and female.

Very distinctive features are a white band round the tail on the buttocks and another encircling the throat from the base of each ear. This species is very similar to the defasa or sing sing waterbuck, except that the defasa has no ring and the inner sides of its buttocks and upper legs are white.

Habitat As the name suggests, waterbuck are usually found near water and where there is plenty of grass in tree- and bush-savannah areas.

Habits Waterbuck live in small herds of about 20 or so. Sometimes several herds will congregate together for short periods. Males have several females and fight off rivals with their magnificent, sweeping horns, which they also use to defend their families from predators. The males are not often attacked except by lions, but young bulls, calves and cows are the prey of cheetahs, leopards and wild dogs. To defend themselves, they frequently leap into the nearest water, submerging themselves with only their nostrils above the surface, the bulls using their great horns like scythes to beat off their attackers. They seem to have no fear of crocodiles and there is a theory that the strong smell coming from glands in their skin wards off crocodiles, although many experts say it serves only to keep off parasites and other biting insects.

Diet The bulk of a waterbuck's diet consists of grass and it particularly likes reedy growth on the edge of dams and swamps. It will also eat some bush leaves.

Breeding Young are born throughout the year, though some authorities say that September, October and November are the most common times. Multiple births are rare.

The First Zebra

(A tale from the Angoni of Central Africa)

In the beginning when all was new on the Earth the animals were all similar, none having special horns or colorful coats. The Creator was busy finishing off his great work and fashioned a multitude of horns of various sizes and shapes and coats of many types and colors. When He had finished He left them in a cave close to the shores of a great lake.

The Creator then sent a message to all the animals living on the grassy plains, that they should go to the cave the next morning and select the horns and coats they thought would suit them best. This caused a great flurry of excitement and anticipation and the animals were all eager to see what the Creator had made for them.

All, that is, except for Zebra, whose only concern in life was food, in fact it was well known among the other animals that Zebra was a glutton. When all the other animals moved off toward the lake at first light, Zebra did not join them. If he was going to take such a long walk he was going to have a good breakfast of luscious grass and he could not see why all the other animals were so carried away with the idea of horns and coats. Although the other animals urged him to hurry along to the cave, Zebra muttered that he would follow on in due course, when he had finished his breakfast. This was done through a mouthful of grass, so the other animals left the ill-mannered Zebra in disgust.

Several hours later Zebra decided he had had his fill, and slowly sauntered off towards the lake, following a broad trail left by the other animals. As

Zebra neared the lake, some of the animals were returning to the plains and Zebra was amazed by their change in appearance. Elephant had chosen a rather drab gray coat, but set this off with a magnificent pair of ivory tusks. Lion had chosen a sleek dusky coat with a regal mane of long black hair. Sable had a glossy black coat and vicious sweeping curved horns.

   One by one Zebra passed all the animals in their brand-new finery. Finally, just as he was about to enter the cave, Zebra passed Rhinoceros. Unfortunately Rhino is very nearsighted; he had chosen a coat several sizes too large and it looked rather baggy on him. Also, he had chosen two horns

that were not the same size and stuck them on his nose. All in all, Rhino looked rather odd but he seemed very pleased with himself.

When Zebra went into the cave the only coat left was a boldly striped black-and-white one and he could find no horns at all. After such a long walk Zebra was feeling quite hungry again so he quickly tried on the remaining coat. This strange black-and-white coat did fit very well and as his belly was rumbling he did not care that it looked different; nor did he mind that no horns were left over for him.

Meanwhile, back on the plains, all the other animals were admiring each other in their brand-new finery. When Zebra got back to the plains he ignored all the others and just put his head down and started chomping away at his lunch. The other animals soon noticed the startling black-and-white coat and so they greeted Zebra with jeers and laughter.

"Look at the greedy Zebra in his funny new coat and without any horns!" cried the Duiker scornfully. Soon all the other animals had taken up the chorus.

Zebra did not care. What did horns matter when all that really counted was plenty of tender green grass to eat whenever he wanted? To this day Zebra has not needed any horns, but he is always fat and glossy in his peculiar black-and-white coat.

How the Zebra got his Stripes

(A Zulu story)

One day long ago, a very big, very fierce baboon came down from the trees to live on the banks of the great Umfolozi River. Here he made his home and declared to all the other animals that the land all around belonged to him, and they were not to use the water in the river. He alone was to be allowed to drink.

There was one among the animals who decided to stand up to fearful Baboon. This was a proud young zebra stallion, Dube.

In those days, zebras were pure white, like the fabled unicorn. Now Dube was brave, and he challenged Baboon to a fight. Baboon, a fierce veteran

of many battles, agreed. He knew all about fighting.

"The loser of the fight," he said, "will be banished forever to the barren kopje across the river." And he told the zebra to come to his kraal the next morning.

The fight was long and terrible. Both animals fought with all their strength, using the weapons the Creator had given them. Dube used his sharp hooves and teeth. Baboon used his long fangs and his agility.

Eventually, Baboon gained the upper hand, and poor Dube was thrown backwards into the blazing logs of the kraal fire. The cruel flames licked all over his body, searing his fine white coat. The dreadful pain gave Dube a surge of new strength, and with a mighty kick he sent Baboon flying. Over the river sailed Baboon, right onto the rocks of the kopje on the other side. Baboon landed with such force that a bald patch remains on his behind to this very day.

But Dube too was marked for life. The burns from the blazing logs in Baboon's fire left black stripes all over his snow-white coat. But at least he had won and from that day on, the water was free to all the animals.

Since then, zebras wear their stripes with pride, and while baboons are banished to stony kopjes, the zebras dwell on the open plains, coming and going to the river just as they please.

FACTS ABOUT ZEBRAS
SPECIES:
BURCHELL'S ZEBRA (Equus burchelli)
Gregarious, in small herds of up to 40.

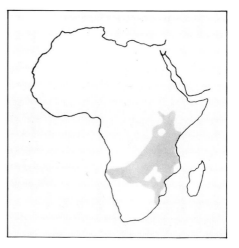

	Male	Female
Height	4 ft	4 ft
Weight	704 lb	616 lb
Weight at Birth	66 lb	66 lb
Age at Weaning	11 months	11 months
Age at Maturity	3 years	3 years
Gestation Period	—	12 months
Number of Young	—	1
Lifespan	20 years	20 years

Identification The zebra is very much like a horse or large pony covered in black-and-white stripes. It is the wild horse of Africa. Although the markings appear the same from a distance, in fact every single zebra's stripes are different.

Habitat Lightly wooded and open grasslands near water.

Habits The zebra is an animal which prefers to run in herds of its own kind, living in groups of up to 40. The male (called a stallion, like a horse) gathers his own group of females around him and fiercely guards them from rivals. Fights between stallions can be heard a long way off; they make fierce noises, barks, and high-pitched whinnies as they rear at each other, kicking and biting with murderous intent.

Sometimes zebras mix with herds of blue wildebeest. The two species eat different types of grass, so they do not compete for food. Both need plenty of water and will travel long distances to get it.

Zebras are one of the lion's favorite prey animals. Their defense is to kick out viciously with their hind hooves. Many a lion has faced a miserable death through starvation because its jawbone has been broken by such a well-aimed kick.

The zebra is a cousin of the horse and the donkey, and its hoof prints and droppings are similar. You might think that its bold black-and-white stripes are the reverse of camouflage — as they are, close up. But at a distance, on the open plains when the heat shimmers up from the ground, the zebra's stripes seem to fade and blur until even a whole herd is almost invisible from a few miles away. The stripes can also be a means of confusing a predator as it moves in close to a running herd. Imagine trying to pick out any one particular zebra from a jumbled mass of moving black-and-white lines!

You will never see a thin-looking zebra because the body fat on a zebra is stored deeper inside the animal, not just under the skin. The only way to tell if a zebra is starving is when its mane starts to flop over to one side, because the one place where fat is stored near the surface, is along the ridge of the neck.

Zoologists have found that zebras actually form close "friendships" with one or two other animals in the herd, and these small groups of "friends" are always together.

Diet Zebras are grazers, but in hard times when grass is scarce they will dig up roots with their front hooves and eat them.

Breeding There is no particular breeding season. Foals are born singly and, amazingly, within a matter of hours from birth, can keep up with the rest of the herd.

How Tsessebe got his Peculiar Horns

(A Bushman story)

Right at the beginning of time, when the Creator, with the help of the great Mantis, was making all the animals, he was faced with an enormous task. There was so much work to do that when He was getting near the end, He was tired and so hurried to finish. In fact, He was in such a rush that He forgot to give Tsessebe any horns!

All the other bucks made fun of poor Tsessebe. Their own heads were proudly decorated with a variety of horns, all different shapes and sizes, but all handsome, graceful and very useful.

Tsessebe was miserable. He wandered alone for a long time, wondering why he had been left out. He avoided contact with the antelopes and gazelles since they would laugh at him. Eventually, he plucked up his courage. He decided that he would go back to the Creator and beg to be given some horns.

The Creator was resting after his great work, and was annoyed at being disturbed. He listened to Tsessebe, and became angry that the mistake should be drawn to His attention.

When Tsessebe had finished his plea, he hung his head and waited. The Creator impatiently grabbed a few twisted old leftover bones, and stuck them on the buck's head.

"Now let's hope you are satisfied!" He said, and sent Tsessebe away.

When the other animals saw Tsessebe's new horns, they made more fun of him than ever. Tsessebe did look very odd — and as their laughter rang out, he was even more miserable.

Being a timid and gentle creature, he did not dare to go back to the Creator again. He decided, sadly, that he would have to be content with what he had; after all, even funny-looking horns were better than no horns at all.

However, the Creator heard the mocking shouts and laughter, and seeing Tsessebe's plight, He took pity and relented. He made Tsessebe a present and gave him the magnificent gifts of speed and agility.

At last, all the other antelope began to envy Tsessebe. Now he runs like the wind and doesn't mind about his horns at all.

FACTS ABOUT TSESSEBE
SPECIES:
TSESSEBE or SASSABY *(Damaliscus lunatus lunatus)*
Gregarious, in small herds of up to 20.
ENDANGERED SPECIES

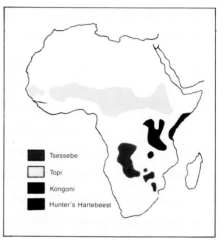

	Male	Female
Height	4 ft	4 ft
Weight	352 lb	319 lb
Weight at Birth	22 lb	22 lb
Age at Weaning	6 months	6 months
Age at Maturity	4 years	3 years
Gestation Period	—	8 months
Number of Young	—	1
Lifespan	12 years	12 years

Map legend:
- Tsessebe
- Topi
- Kongoni
- Hunter's Hartebeest

Identification Tsessebe is one of the larger antelopes, with a long face, sloping back and humped shoulders. The horns are crescent-shaped with very pronounced rings. Color is purplish chocolate-brown, with bare patches beneath the eyes and dark gray-black smudges on thighs and shoulders. Both sexes have horns.

Habitat Open grasslands and swampy floodplains.

Habits The tsessebe is the fastest antelope in southern Africa. It can outrun all but the swiftest of predators, and has been clocked at 37 miles per hour (60 km per hour) — as fast as a top racehorse. Tsessebe are normally found near wildebeest and zebra and, like them, prefer open areas. They are also herd animals, like their cousin the wildebeest. Tsessebe have the peculiar habit of standing stock-still on top of anthills for a long time. They do this to show other tsessebe that this territory belongs to them. It probably also helps them to look out for predators.

Diet They graze almost entirely on grass.

Breeding Calves are usually born singly in September and October.

Why the Wart Hog goes about on his Knees

(A Zulu story)

Wart hog had made himself a lovely, spacious home in an old anteater hole. He had built it up and made a wide entrance, and thought it was quite the grandest hole in the area. But one day Wart hog looked out and was horrified to see a lion stalking stealthily towards his cave.

Thinking quickly, he pretended to be supporting the roof of his hole with his strong back, pushing up with his tusks. "Help!" he cried to the lion, "I am going to be crushed! The roof is caving in! Perhaps you had better flee, O Lion!"

However, the lion had been caught out once before with a trick like this (remember sly old Jackal?), and he was not going to be fooled a second time. He roared so fiercely that Wart hog dropped to his knees, trembling, and begged for mercy. Luckily for him, Lion was not really all that hungry. Also, he was amused to think the slow-witted wart hog would try to copy Jackal's trick. So he pardoned the wart hog and left, saying, "Stay on your knees, you foolish beast!"

Wart hog took this to be an order and that is why, even today, you will see Wart hog feeding on his knees, in a very undignified position, with his bottom up in the air and his snout snuffling in the dust.

Why Wart Hog Is So Ugly

(A story from East Africa)

In the beginning, Wart hog was a small but handsome beast. Unfortunately he was also despised by all the other inhabitants of the savannah because he was vain and rude. Even Hare could not tolerate Wart hog's superior attitude.

One thing Wart hog had learned from the start was how to make himself a comfortable home. These were usually old anteater holes, no longer required by the original owner, and with some alteration and enlarging they were ideal.

In this snug, comfortable home he was safe from prowling hunters at night, and during the day he never ventured too far from safety. This retreat was needed quite frequently because Wart hog's rudeness meant that he was often scurrying to safety.

Bright and early one morning Wart hog was out enjoying a meal. He was feeding on roots and grass shoots with his bottom sticking up in the air in a most undignified manner, so busy eating that he failed to notice Porcupine.

After a night of walking around searching for food Porcupine was exhausted and, seeing an inviting-looking hole, quickly scurried down the passage and was soon curled up in the main chamber of Wart hog's hole, sound asleep.

After several hours of feeding, Wart hog trotted off to the nearby waterhole and had a good wallow in the mud. Feeling much refreshed, he was about to head off to find more grazing when he noticed Lion strolling by. Unable to resist the temptation Wart hog passed some very rude remarks about Lion's mane looking very messy and unkempt. This was too much for Lion, who had far too many tricks played on him, and too many undignified remarks from such a rude little fellow. So Lion charged Wart hog, hoping to catch him and teach him a lesson that he would never forget.

Seeing the enraged Lion bearing down on him, Wart hog was seized by panic and sprinted off towards his den. A great chase ensued, but eventually Wart hog arrived safely at his home and shot down the tunnel. Lion was left to stand guard at the top.

Meanwhile, Porcupine, who had been fast asleep, woke with a start, sure that some predator had found her down the hole and was coming to grab her. Jumping to her feet, Porcupine braced herself for an attack, spreading out her long, sharp quills. Wart hog, unable to stop, came bursting through into the chamber, straight into Porcupine. Wart hog got a face full of sharp, painful quills.

Lion was startled to hear a great yelp of pain come from Wart hog's den. There was the sound of a considerable commotion from under the ground and then Wart hog shot out of the tunnel, screaming and howling in pain. He had a dozen or so quills sticking out of his cheeks, nose and forehead, plus the signs of a great many more puncture holes.

Lion saw and heard the obvious discomfort of Wart hog and decided that he might have learned his lesson and so left him to his pain.

Wart hog was most miserable, especially as none of the animals would help him pull out the quills, remembering how rude and vain he had been in the past. Wart hog's face swelled up and was sore for a very long time.

To this day Wart hog is covered in warts and bumps and he is no longer handsome. Taught his lesson, he is now a humble animal who minds his own business. As if reminded of his painful experience, Wart hog now enters his den backwards to protect his face from further damage.

FACTS ABOUT WART HOGS
SPECIES:
WART HOG *(Phacochoerus aethiopicus)*
Found in pairs and small family groups.

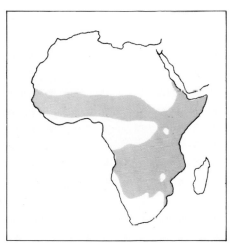

	Male	Female
Height	29 in	28 in
Weight	154 lb	132 lb
Weight at Birth	1¾ lb	1¾ lb
Age at Weaning	3 months	3 months
Age at Maturity	2 years	14 months
Gestation Period	—	4½ months
Number of Young	—	3-7
Lifespan	12 years	12 years

Identification There is no mistaking the wart hog with its curved upper tusks, large ugly facial "warts" and gray body. It is hairless except for the bristles on the cheeks and shoulders, dark erect mane and bristly tail tip. Both sexes have tusks.

Habitat They live near water in open tree- and shrub-grasslands.

Habits Living in small family groups (mother, father and young), they are frequently seen because, unlike many other animals, they drink during the day, often when the sun is at its highest. They frequently use abandoned anteater holes and other burrows as lairs toward which they will bolt when frightened, holding their thin tails upright like radar antennae presenting a most amusing sight. They enter the lair backwards, so their sharp tusks face out and can be used to fend off attacking animals.

Their main enemies are lions, leopards, cheetahs, hyenas and packs of wild dogs.

Like domestic pigs, they have poor eyesight but an excellent sense of smell and hearing. Despite their ferocious appearance wart hogs are not really aggressive unless cornered.

Diet They are grazers and root-eaters, feeding mostly on short grass and whole plants, roots and all. They have a habit of shuffling along on their front knees when foraging.

Breeding The average wart hog litter consists of three or four piglets, although up to eight have been observed.

The Race that was Rigged

(A Swazi story)

Tortoise was eating peacefully one day, minding his own business, when along came Mofuli, the hare. Mofuli, like all wicked little hares, could not resist the chance to make fun of Tortoise and tease him about how slow and ponderous he was.

Mofuli, full of mischief, challenged Tortoise to a race. There were some palm trees about 550 yards (500 metres) from where they were, and Mofuli said that was where they would race to.

Tortoise had had enough of Mofuli, and all hares, to last him a lifetime, since this was not the first time he had been teased by one of these irritating creatures. He wished he could put Hare in his place once and for all.

He thought for a moment and then said, "Speed is not everything, Mofuli. One must have endurance, too. Let us make this a real race — a long one. Let us race to the Blue Pan, some six miles (ten kilometres) from here. And, so that I have time to prepare, let us run the race in five days' time, at noon."

Mofuli was most surprised. He hadn't expected Tortoise to accept the challenge, and had been looking forward to a good long teasing. But he was scornful, and he almost decided not to bother with the race. But Tortoise was so much in earnest, that in the end he agreed. And Hare went on his way, laughing. He could hardly wait to tell all the other animals about the silly old Tortoise.

But Tortoise lost no time. He called on his relatives for help, telling them about his plan. It was very simple: at noon on Saturday, they were to place themselves in different positions all along the path that Hare and Tortoise were to race. Every one of them was to run toward Blue Pan, starting from different points along the route. All they had to do was to keep going as fast as they could, until Hare had sped past, and then they could go home and rest if they wanted to.

Tortoise collected a gourd to hold water, and set off for the pan that very day. It took him almost five days to get to Blue Pan, but at last he arrived. At noon on Saturday, he filled his gourd with water and settled down to wait.

Meanwhile, Mofuli had arrived at the starting point at the agreed time, and there he found Tortoise's cousin. It did not occur to Mofuli that this was a different tortoise. They greeted each other, and the race began.

Mofuli was out of sight in a twinkling, and Tortoise's cousin plodded off on his way, chuckling to himself. Mofuli was laughing too, until he reached the first rise and there was Tortoise ahead of him! (Actually, it was Tortoise's brother, stumbling along as fast as he could go.) Mofuli ran faster and soon he was out of sight. He was rather puzzled, and as the race went on, he became more and more confused.

Over each hill, Mofuli found Tortoise in front of him. Each time he overtook him, running like the wind, Tortoise would laugh loudly. By now, Hare was thinking that Tortoise must have learned to fly.

It was very hot, being midday, and the sun beat down. The pan was still two miles (three kilometres) away, and Mofuli was terribly thirsty. He came over the next rise to find Tortoise, ahead of him again!

In desperation, Mofuli put on his last burst of speed. Heart pounding, he strained every muscle, and at last came in sight of the Blue Pan. He was almost at the pan, when suddenly he tripped and fell. He lay on the ground, exhausted — he could go no further. His sides were heaving and every limb was trembling.

After a few moments he staggered to his feet. He looked up and what do you think he saw?

Why, Tortoise, of course, walking towards him from the pan, carrying a gourd of cool, clear water. This sight was more than Mofuli could stand. He fainted from shock and exhaustion.

Tortoise revived Hare by sprinkling cold water over his face. When Mofuli came round, Tortoise said in a soothing voice, "Drink this, my poor friend. I had an idea that you might be needing it. The endurance of some animals is not quite what they claim it to be." And he chuckled quietly to himself.

So it was that slow old Tortoise beat Hare at his own game. Clever as he was, Mofuli did not have the brains to see that he himself had at last been made a fool of.

The Tug-of-War

(A Ndebele story)

One peaceful morning a hare called Umvundla, who lived by the Zambezi River, was bored. He felt like creating a bit of fun for himself, so he looked around to see what he could do. Suddenly, he spotted two dignified old residents of the area — Rhino and Hippo.

Now Hippo, although aware of his ugliness, was very proud of his strength. Umvundla hopped up to the river bank and called: "O mighty one! Why do you say you are so strong? Even I, with my small size and thin legs, could beat you in a tug-of-war!"

Hippo ignored Hare with his ridiculous boasting. But Umvundla kept pestering him.

At last Hippo replied, in the hope of getting some peace and quiet, "A tug-of-war? All right, I will show you, my little long-eared nuisance."

Umvundla danced with delight. He pointed to an old, rounded dome of earth beyond the river bank. "I bet I could pull you clear out of the water and over that termite hill," he taunted.

Umvundla then dashed off to braid a long, strong rope. When he came back, he tied one end to Hippo's hind leg, saying, "When I shout, 'Pull', from behind the hill you must pull with all your might, for I shall surely beat you!"

Hippo thought that Umvundla's foolishness had at last got the better of him. He said nothing, and settled down again in the water. In the warm shallows, he soon dozed off.

Now Umvundla took the other end of the rope, and crept around to the other side of the hill, where he knew that old bull Rhino was asleep in the shade. He picked up some fierce little red ants from a nearby hole and quietly dropped them in Rhino's ear. Rhino awoke with a grunt, and shook his head, trying to scratch his ears.

"Good morning!" piped Umvundla, "I was just coming to warn you of the ant's nest. Oh, I see one has crawled into your ear — may I help you to remove it? And with a great pretence of concern, he actually pushed the ants in further.

"That was most kind of you," said the unsuspecting Rhino, "Your small feet are just right, while mine are far too large for the job. You've no idea what trouble I have with ants." And on he grumbled, in the way of cranky old men everywhere.

"Well!" replied the cheeky Umvundla, "My feet may be small, but they are very strong. Stronger than yours, in fact. I'll show you just how strong I really am. I challenge you to a tug-of-war! I bet I can pull you right over this anthill and into the river!"

Old Rhino snorted with laughter. But at last he, too, was pestered into playing Umvundla's game. So Hare tied the other end of his rope around Rhino's hind leg. Then he hurried to the top of the hill. He hid in a little hollow, and called loudly, "PULL!"

As he shouted, the ants began to bite deep inside Rhino's ear, and with a bellow of pain, Rhino charged off.

Poor old Hippo had forgotton about Umvundla. He was dozing peacefully in his pool when there was a sudden, hard tug on his hind leg. Before he knew it, he was dragged out of the river and halfway up the hill.

When Hippo realized what was happening, he dug in his heels and gave a mighty heave, and the great tug-of-war started in earnest.

Each of the powerful animals strained with every muscle, and worked themselves up into a fine fury. Umvundla laughed so much that he fell over and went rolling down the side of the anthill. When they saw him, the two great animals knew they had been tricked.

Roaring with anger, they charged after Umvundla, hoping to trample him into the dust before he could tell the other animals how foolish they had been.

As they charged, the hare waited until the last possible moment, and then skipped out of the way. Hippo and Rhino were going so fast they couldn't stop. With a tremendous crash, they met head-on, hurting each other terribly. In a blind rage, they started to fight each other — until they heard Umvundla, who by this time was weeping with laughter.

Umvundla realized that at last the game was up, so he jumped up and sped off into the bush. He could hardly wait to tell the other animals how he had made fools of Hippo and Rhino.

To this day, Rhino thinks the little red ants are still in his ears. (Some say that the ants are so far down that they live in his brain, and this is why Rhino is so bad-tempered.)

As for Hippo, you will find him still searching the river banks at night, hoping to find Umvundla and throw him to the hungry crocodiles.

FACTS ABOUT HARES
SPECIES:
SCRUB HARE (*Lepus saxatilis*)
Solitary.

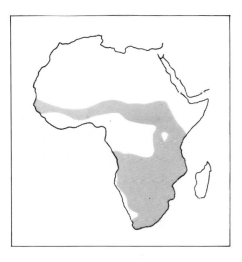

	Male	Female
Height	6 in	6 in
Weight	5½ lb	4¼ lb
Weight at Birth	¼ lb	¼ lb
Age at Weaning	1 month	1 month
Age at Maturity	8 months	8 months
Gestation Period	—	1 month
Number of Young	—	usually 2
Lifespan	5 years	5 years

Identification Very similar to the hares of Europe, America and other parts of the world. The scrub hare is one of many species common in Africa. It has long ears, strong hind legs which are longer than the front ones, and a white tail with a thick black stripe down the middle.

Habitat Dry, open country and sparse woodlands.

Habits The hare is usually nocturnal, hiding during the day in thick scrub or grass.

The hare is grass-colored and, by lying very still, avoids being noticed. However, if you are about to step upon a hare it will suddenly burst out from cover and run, zigzagging, until it is out of sight; this makes it very difficult to catch. Hares are preyed upon by eagles, owls, pythons and many other animals; including cheetahs, which are the only animals fast enough to run a hare down. Other hunters have to creep up close and make a surprise attack.

In African folklore, the hare is often the star of the story. He is portrayed as a creature who is always playing pranks and causing mischief. He is a boaster, always saying how clever he is, especially at making the high-and-mighty animals look silly. Hare always seems to come out on top!

Diet Hares feed on a variety of grasses, from which they also get enough moisture and so don't need to live near water.

Breeding Mother hares usually bear only two young at a time. Unlike rabbits, they do not live in holes, but make a shallow nest in the middle of a thick clump of grass, where the babies are left, keeping as still as stones, while the mother is out feeding.

Why the Dassie has no Tail

(A Xhosa fable)

Long ago at the dawn of time, and long before man appeared, the Lion was the King of all the animals, and furthermore, he was the only one to possess a tail.

Now, although he was very proud of the honor bestowed upon him by the Creator, he felt that his subjects should also have tails, as tails were so useful — and also because then Lion himself would not be such an odd man out. He made up his mind to make some tails himself, and give them to his subjects.

So, setting to work, he made tails of all shapes, sizes and colors. When he had finished, he told Baboon to call all the animals together, so that they might choose for themselves. Baboon was told to bring them all to Lion's Council Rock, and to make sure he forgot no one.

Baboon set off to call all, far and wide, and by nightfall they had started to assemble at the Council Rock. All, that is, except the lazy little Dassie. He felt that it was much too far to go. However, Dassie asked some passing monkeys to collect his present for him, and to explain to the King that he felt too ashamed to appear before Lion, as he was so small and humble. Satisfied that his message would be passed on safely, Dassie turned back into his cave and continued with his nap.

The old King Lion handed out tails to all the assembled animals, passing them over as each animal pointed to the one he had chosen. But Lion

made many mistakes due to his failing eyesight, in spite of a full, bright moon. (That is why, today, the squirrel has a tail much longer than his own body, while the elephant has such an embarrassingly short, thin tail.)

When most of the tails had been handed out, Lion noticed that Dassie was missing. The animals were all busy congratulating each other and comparing tails, when finally the monkeys, chattering noisily, remembered to pass on the Dassie's message. The King was very angry at the Dassie for disobeying the summons, but eventually he relented and picked out a small, furry tail for the monkeys to take back for Dassie. For after all, the King wanted all the animals to have a tail.

However, on their way back, the monkeys decided to teach the lazy Dassie a lesson, for they thought that Dassie did not deserve his present. So they stuck the little furry tail on to the end of their own brand new, long tails. They were rather pleased with the result.

On reaching Dassie's rocky home in a kopje, the monkeys showed off their gifts, parading about this way and that. They told the lazy Dassie what they had done to teach him a lesson. In future, they said, the Dassie was to obey the King, and stop being so idle.

Poor Dassie was most upset — but was far too lazy to do anything about it. So that is why, to this day, the dassie still has no tail.

FACTS ABOUT DASSIES
SPECIES:
DASSIE or ROCK HYRAX *(Procavia capensis)*
Gregarious, living in colonies of up to 200.

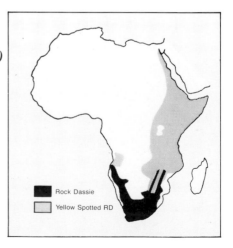

	Male	Female
Height	8 in	8 in
Weight	8¾ lb	6⅔ lb
Weight at Birth	½ lb	⅜ lb
Age at Weaning	4 months	4 months
Age at Maturity	12 months	12 months
Gestation Period	—	7½ months
Number of Young	—	2 or 3
Lifespan	7 years	7 years

Rock Dassie

Yellow Spotted RD

Identification Plumpish little animals with a rounded head and small ears, short legs, no visible tail and a thick furry coat. Also known as rock rabbits, they are about the size of a large rabbit. However, unlike rabbits they are not rodents but are considered to be more closely related to the elephant!

Habitat Dassies live in colonies, and are always found among caves and crevices in kopjes or rock outcrops.

Habits Small, stiff hairs cover the pads of the dassie's feet, enabling it to scamper across smooth rock faces or along the branches of trees, without falling.

Dassies make a noise like a shrill bark or howl, and their alarm call is a whistle to warn others in the colony of approaching danger. They retreat into cracks and small caves where it is difficult for a predator to reach them.

Dassies are preyed upon by leopards, black eagles, pythons and other animals. Where there is human habitation, the dassie population is usually in danger, for their fur pelts are greatly prized for use as warm winter jackets.

Diet Although dassies have very long front fangs, they are vegetarian, feeding on leaves, grass, fruit and twigs. The fangs are their only weapon of defense and can give a very nasty bite.

Breeding A mother dassie usually only produces two babies a year, so they cannot keep up numbers in their colonies as fast as rabbits.

The Foolishness of the Ostrich

(A Bushman legend)

At the beginning of time, Mantis (the Creator's assistant) was doubtful about giving fire to the world. He was afraid that any being that had the use of fire might destroy himself with it. So he decided to give Ostrich the job of guarding fire so that no one could play with it. He thought to himself, "If any being can get the fire away from loyal and stubborn Ostrich, then they are obviously clever enough to use the fire wisely." And, satisfied with this arrangement, he gave Ostrich his strictest instructions and returned to the heavens.

Ostrich kept the fire well-hidden under one of his wings, but the first Bushman discovered where he was keeping it. The Bushman wanted the fire; he wanted it to cook his food with, to keep him warm at night, and to keep away the nighttime predators. How fine it would be for him and his family to have some fire! So the Bushman decided to make a plan to steal away the fire from Ostrich.

The next day, the Bushman, who even then could talk to the animals, went up to Ostrich and greeted him politely. Ostrich stared at him suspiciously, but returned the greeting.

"O fine and wise Ostrich," said the Bushman, "O greatest of all the birds. I have good news for you!"

"Oh yes?" said Ostrich, interested.

"Indeed, magnificent one," replied the Bushman, "I had a wonderful dream last night. I dreamed that you could fly!"

Ostrich looked annoyed. "How so?" he demanded.

"I dreamed that you would be given the gift of flight if you stood with wings outstretched in the strong wind before dawn. The dream told me that if you kept your eyes closed and wings out, you would then take off and soar like an eagle!"

Ostrich couldn't resist the thought of being able to fly. It was his dearest wish. And so the very next day, at dawn he stood high on a hilltop in the chill dawn wind, wings outstretched and eyes squeezed shut.

While he stood there, the Bushman crept up and snatched the fire from its hiding place, and made off as fast as he could.

Thus was man given the greatest gift of all from Mantis.

Ostrich was so upset at losing the fire, and from the disappointment of not being able to fly, that he became feeble-minded. In fact, he became such a silly bird that now he has to leave one or two eggs outside the nest while he is sitting on them, to remind him what he is supposed to be doing!

Why Ostrich has a Long Neck

(A Sesotho story)

Once upon a time Ostrich had a normal-sized neck, just like other birds. In those days, Ostrich and Crocodile were friends. All the other animals warned Ostrich that Crocodile was an evil animal, and not to be trusted. But Ostrich, for such a big bird, has a small head and few brains, so he took no notice.

One day Crocodile was very hungry, as he hadn't eaten for several days. None of the animals had dared to come near his pan, for fear of being caught and dragged into the water.

So Crocodile said to Ostrich, "My dear friend, a tooth of mine is aching. I have so many teeth — there always seems to be something wrong with one of them. Please put your head inside my mouth and see if you can tell me which one it is." And he opened his jaws, wide.

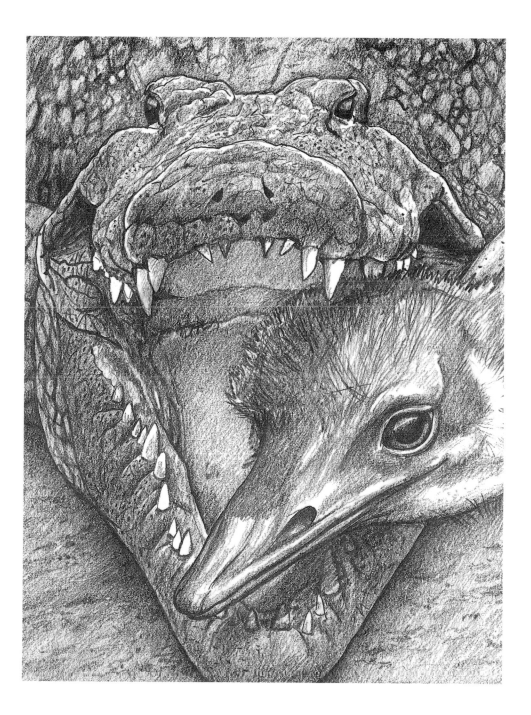

Foolish Ostrich did as he was asked, and wicked Crocodile closed his mouth on the bird's head. Then Crocodile started to pull backwards, into the water, where Ostrich would drown and thus make a fine meal for him.

But Ostrich, although stupid, was a large bird and very strong. He did not want to die, and so he pulled in the opposite direction.

Both were equally determined to win this fight, and as they pulled and pulled, Ostrich's neck started to stretch and stretch. It grew longer and longer, and must have been very painful for poor old Ostrich, but he did not give in.

At last Crocodile got tired and let go. Poor Ostrich ran away, and ever since then he has lived in sandy places, far away from rivers. He still has a long neck and he never, never goes near crocodiles.

The Ostrich and her Chicks

(A tale from the Masai)

Long ago a pair of ostriches, having laid a large clutch of eggs, hatched them, and started to rear them.

Soon after, a passing lion noticed the chicks while they were left unattended by their parents, and so took them. Lion hid them in his den, intending to eat them one by one. Finding her chicks gone Ostrich followed their tracks to Lion's den and demanded her chicks back, but Lion refused and chased her away.

Ostrich went to the Council of Elders and pleaded for their help, but they were afraid of Lion and decided that the chicks were the Lion's children. Very much disappointed, Ostrich called a meeting of the other animals to be held at a large ant heap in front of Lion's den. At this ant heap Mongoose lived in a hole he had dug himself, which had two exits.

When all the animals had collected at the ant heap they too became afraid of Lion and agreed that the chicks were Lion's children. At this point Mongoose spoke out, saying, "Well, I for one have never seen an animal with hairs have young with feathers. Think what you may, the chicks belong to Ostrich!"

Lion was furious to have a mere mongoose challenge his authority and leapt at Mongoose, intending to kill him as an example to the other animals. Mongoose was too quick for Lion, however, and jumped down his hole in the ant heap. Safe from Lion, he ran through his tunnels and escaped out of the other hole, which Lion did not know about.

The enraged lion stood guard over the hole and, although he grew hungry Lion did not dare go away for fear that Mongoose would escape. Not only did he still believe that Mongoose was trapped underground, but he still wanted to teach the other animals a lesson they would never forget.

Lion was so determined he did not leave his post for several days until he fainted from hunger and fatigue. At last Ostrich was able to run into Lion's den and rescue her chicks. She was eternally grateful to the cunning little mongoose.

Mind you, to this day Ostrich is still very forgetful and her chicks have to be able to look after themselves soon after hatching.

FACTS ABOUT OSTRICHES
SPECIES:
OSTRICH (Struthio camelus)

Usually in pairs. Young are gregarious.

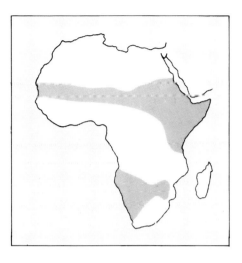

	Male	Female
Height	6¾ ft	6 ft
Weight	308 lb	264 lb
Weight at Hatching	3⅓ lb	3⅓ lb
Age at Maturity	8 years	8 years
Incubation Period	45 days — incubation shared	
Number of Eggs	—	12-20
Lifespan	50 years	50 years

Identification The ostrich is the largest bird on earth. Standing tall on long, bare legs, it also has a long, curving, predominantly white neck. The humped body of the male is covered in black patches and the wings and tail are tipped with white. The female is brown and white. Ostriches are flightless but can run very fast — up to 44 miles per hour (70 km per hour).

Habitat The ostrich is found in the drier areas of southern Africa.

Habits Ostriches are preyed upon by lions and cheetahs, and many smaller predators also eat the chicks and eggs if they get a chance. The chicks, however, have very good camouflage, and are able to run quite fast soon after hatching.

The adults use their powerful legs not only to run fast to escape enemies, but as weapons to keep attackers at bay. They tend to live in small, scattered groups or sometimes singly.

Diet Ostriches are mainly vegetarian, eating grass, succulents, berries and seeds, though they will also eat insects. They swallow large numbers of pebbles which help grind the harder food in the gizzard.

Breeding Ostriches normally mate for life, and they share the task of incubating the eggs. The male, which has mostly black feathers, sits on the eggs at night, and the drab, brown female covers them during the day. In this way, the nest is much harder to see.

The female does not make a nest of any sort, laying up to 20 eggs in a bare, shallow dip in the ground. Once the young ones hatch, it is usually the male ostrich which looks after the chicks until they are old enough to fend for themselves.

The Living Stones

(A Swazi legend)

The Creator, who made all the animals, also made a pair of creatures known as living stones, because they looked so much like a pair of cracked, brown rocks. These were, of course, Tortoise and his wife.

The Tortoises lived together for many, many years. But to their sorrow, they didn't have any children. Year after year went by, and each year the

Tortoises hoped that this would be the year that they would have young.

Finally, the husband Tortoise went to the Creator, and humbly asked if their greatest wish could be granted. Their long, long years together, he said, had been empty without any young of their own.

The Creator told Tortoise that he and his wife were, by then, too old to have children. Tortoise's wife would surely die from the strain, He said. The Tortoises must be content with each other's companionship.

Tortoise and his wife were greatly disappointed. After a while, Tortoise thought to himself, "Surely the Great One is mistaken. If we do not have young ones, who will follow us? And like the rocks we resemble, surely we must be ageless." So back he went to the Creator. But his plea was met with the same reply.

Now Tortoise really was convinced that the Creator must be wrong. Finally he threw himself at the Great One's feet, for the third and last time.

The Creator was moved at Tortoise's courage, persistence and sorrow, so He let the couple have their young ones.

He also gave Tortoise the following advice: "Tell your wife to take very good care of herself. She is really much too old to produce eggs. But when her time comes for egg-laying, she must watch the eggs carefully. She must

keep them warm, but not let them get too hot. She must protect them with her body until they hatch."

Old Tortoise was overjoyed, and rushed home with the good news. But he did not mention that the strain might kill his wife. He instructed her on the care of her eggs, and she carefully followed the advice of the Creator. She ate well, took care to rest a lot, and did no heavy work.

She managed to lay the eggs without too much trouble, and after the incubation time was over, and four lovely baby tortoises were hatched, she looked after them just as the Creator had advised.

However, as in all matters, the Great One was right. The old mother tortoise, taxed beyond her strength, died. The bereaved husband did his best to care for his young ones, but soon he too died, of a broken heart.

The Great One looked down with pity upon the orphaned babies, and decided to care for them Himself. He guided each to food, and provided for them.

And now, no mother tortoise ever has to care for her eggs, or her babies; for the Creator ordered the Sun to warm the eggs, and when tortoise babies are hatched, each one is able to take care of itself. The Creator shows it where to find food, and how to hide inside its shell when danger threatens.

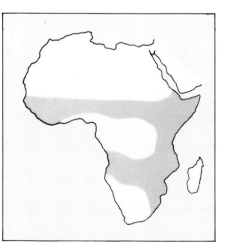

FACTS ABOUT TORTOISES
SPECIES:
HINGED TORTOISE *(Kinixys bellania bellania)*
Solitary.

	Male	Female
Length	8 in	8¾ in
Weight	3⅓ lb	4½ lb
Length at Hatching	1½ in	1½ in
Age at Maturity	8 years	8 years
Incubation Period	12 months	12 months
Number of Eggs	—	2 or 3
Lifespan	20 years	20 years

Identification The tortoise is a relative of the turtle. Both have a body encased in a shell of bone covered by horny shields. They can retract the head, limbs and tail inside this shell. There are no teeth in the jaw, which instead has a horny cutting edge.

Habitat Southern Africa possesses a great many species of tortoise, living in many different environments. Some live in the water and are known as terrapins. Southern Africa hosts the world's greatest variety of land tortoises.

Habits During winter most tortoises hibernate in snug-fitting holes which they dig in old termite mounds or banks of earth. There they stay until the first rains of summer, when they wake up. Their worst enemy is the bush fire, because they move too slowly to get out of the way. They are also prey for many predators; including eagles, which have learned to drop them from a height in order to break the shell.

Diet Tortoises are vegetarian, eating most kinds of grass, succulent plants, fungi and fallen fruit. They have been seen gnawing at old bones, probably to obtain minerals and sharpen the jaw rather than as food.

Breeding They mate when the first rains come and the female lays six to 12 eggs in a hole that she has dug. The hole is then covered over and smoothed down. The young, which hatch in the next rainy season, are born complete with a shell and are ready to fend for themselves immediately.

GLOSSARY

Baobab
A tree widely distributed throughout the drier, low-lying areas of Africa. These long-lived trees are distinctive because of their huge girth, smooth bark and cream-of-tartar seed pods.

Browser
An animal that eats mainly from trees and shrubs, taking leaves, twigs and shoots, rather than grazing or eating grass.

Bush
A general term applied to areas in southern Africa that still resemble the natural or original state.

Calabash
See Gourd.

Carnivore
An animal that lives by eating other animals.

Diurnal
Term describing an animal that is active during the hours of daylight. (*See also* Nocturnal.)

Ecology
The study of the relationship between living things and their environment, including both their non-living surroundings and other animals.

Endangered
A term applied to an animal that is threatened with extinction, usually due to pressure from mankind either directly (from over-hunting and poaching) or indirectly (by changing the creature's habitat). The World Wildlife Fund's "Red List" is a list of the animals most threatened with extinction.

Extinction
When a species no longer exists either in the wild or in captivity it is said to be extinct. Extinction is forever!

Gemsbok cucumber
The fruit of a creeping plant, common in many dry areas. This fruit, although bitter, contains a lot of moisture and is important to man and wildlife in the dry season.

Gestation Period
The period of time required for a mammal to develop in its mother's womb from the date of conception through to birth.

Gourd
The dried and hollowed-out shell of a fruit related to the melon. In Africa gourds are widely used as water containers and drinking vessels.

140

Grazer	An animal that feeds on grass.
Gregarious	A gregarious animal is one that lives in flocks or herds.
Habitat	The immediate surroundings of a creature or plant, that normally provide everything it requires to live.
Herbivore	An animal that feeds on plants.
Heritage	Our natural heritage is the natural environment left to us by our ancestors and which we are entrusted to hand on to future generations.
Hibernate	A creature hibernates when it spends time in a deep sleep or torpor to avoid harsh climatic conditions such as cold winters.
Honey-guide	A small brown bird that eats insect larvae and grubs. It has the peculiar habit of guiding man and honey-badgers to beehives in the bush. It then eats the leftovers.
Hunter-gatherer	A term applied to nomadic tribes such as the Bushmen of southern Africa who live off the land rather than relying on crops and livestock.
Incubation period	The period of time required for a bird or reptile to develop in its egg from the time the egg is laid until the day it hatches.
Inganga	A southern African name for a witch doctor.
Kopje	An Afrikaans name used throughout southern Africa to describe a small rocky hill or outcrop.
Kraal	Either an area protected by a stockade or fence, for containing livestock; or a village.
Leguaan	*See* Water-monitor.
Mammals	A term for the group of animals that are warm-blooded, have milk-producing glands, are partly covered in hair and normally bear their young alive. This group includes man, elephant, baboon and bats.

Migrate	Animals migrate when they undertake seasonal movements, often covering long distances, because of variations in food or water supplies due to changing seasons.
Muti	A southern African term for traditional medicines.
Nocturnal	A nocturnal creature is one that is active by night. (*See also* Diurnal.)
Omnivore	A creature that eats both meat and vegetation.
Oxpecker	A small African bird closely related to the starling. It is so named because it sits on the backs of cattle and eats ticks and other insects.
Pan	A natural waterhole.
Predator	An animal that catches other animals for food.
Prey	Any animal caught by a predator.
Pride	A family group of lions.
Resource	Something available as a stock or reserve that can be used when needed.
Reptile	A cold-blooded animal with scaly skin, e.g. snakes and lizards.
Sanctuary	A safe place, such as a national park, where animals are usually free from threat.
Savannah	Extensive areas of natural grassland.
Scavenger	An animal that lives off the dead remains of other animals or plants, e.g. jackals and vultures, which scavenge from the remains of lion kills.
Solitary	A solitary animal is one that lives alone, without companions for most of the time.
Species	A term, singular or plural, for a group of animals or plants with common characteristics and which do not breed with others.

Territory   An area used by an animal for feeding and/or breeding, often defended against its own kind and sometimes against other species too.

Tsamma melon   A creeping plant found in dry areas. Its large fruit contain moist, pulpy seeds and are an important food source to man and wildlife in the dry season.

Umbrella tree   A large, flat-topped acacia common in many areas of Africa.

Veld   *See* Bush.

Vlei   An Afrikaans name widely used in southern Africa for an area of marshy ground.

Wallow   A mud- or dust-bath in which animals lie and roll to cool off and obtain protection from skin parasites such as ticks and lice.

Water-monitor   A large lizard, growing up to 6¾ ft (2 m) long, common throughout most of Africa and closely associated with rivers and dams.

Weaning   The stage at which a young animal is no longer dependent on its mother's milk and starts to eat the same food as the adult.

BIBLIOGRAPHY

AFRICAN MYTHS AND LEGENDS. Kathleen Arnott, Oxford University Press, 1962
ANIMALS OF RHODESIA. Astley Maberly, Howard Timmins, 1963.
BANTU FOLKLORE. Matthew L. Hewat, M.D., T. Maskew Miller, 1906
BIRDS OF SOUTH AFRICA. Austin Roberts, The Trustees of the John Voelker Bird Book Fund. Distributed by C. Struik, 4th ed., 2nd imp., 1978
COMMON SNAKES OF SOUTH AFRICA. John Visser, Purnell & Sons, 1979
FIELD GUIDE TO THE LARGER MAMMALS OF AFRICA. Jean Dorst and Pierre Dandelot, Collins, 2nd ed., 1972
LEGENDARY AFRICA. Sue Fox, Everton Offset, 1977
MAMMALS OF THE KRUGER AND OTHER NATIONAL PARKS. H. Kumpf; a publication of the National Parks Board of Trustees of the Republic of South Africa.
MATABELE FIRESIDE TALES. Phyllis Savory, Howard Timmins, 1962
MYTHS AND LEGENDS OF SOUTHERN AFRICA. Penny Miller, T.V. Bulpin, 1979
SIGNS OF THE WILD. Clive Walker, Natural History Publications, 1981
SOUTH AFRICAN FOLK TALES. James A. Honey, M.D., Baker & Taylor, 1960
SPECIMENS OF BUSHMAN FOLKLORE. W.H.I. Bleek and L.C. Lloyd, C. Struik, 1968
SWAZI FIRESIDE TALES. Phyllis Savory, Howard Timmins, 1973
TALES FROM THE OKAVANGO. Thomas J. Larson, Howard Timmins, 1972
THE BIRDS OF AFRICA. Vol. I, Leslie Brown, Emil Urban and Kenneth Newman, Academic Press, 1982
THE BUSHMAN SPEAKS. Mary Philips, Howard Timmins, 1961
THE GAME ANIMALS OF SOUTHERN AFRICA. C.T. Astley Maberly, Nelson, 1963
THE MAMMALS OF RHODESIA, ZAMBIA AND MALAWI. Reay H.N. Smithers and E.J. Bierley, Collins, 1966.
THE MAMMALS OF THE SOUTHERN AFRICAN SUBREGION. Reay H.N. Smithers, University of Pretoria, 1983
XHOSA FIRESIDE TALES. Phyllis Savory, Howard Timmins, 1963
ZULU FIRESIDE TALES. Phyllis Savory, Howard Timmins, 1961

Wild Dog

Hippopotamus

Waterbuck

Baboon